SCHOLASTIC

GRADE 3

AF650316

Great Math Practice

Previously published as Scholastic Great Math Practices by Scholastic

Published by Scholastic India Pvt. Ltd.

A subsidiary of Scholastic Inc., New York, 10012 (USA).

Publishers since 1920, with international operations in Canada, Australia, New Zealand, the United Kingdom, India and Hong Kong.

For information regarding permission, write to:
Scholastic India Pvt. Ltd.
A-27, Ground Floor, Bharti Sigma Centre
Infocity - 1, Sector 34, Gurgaon (Haryana) 122001
Email: education@scholastic.co.in

First edition: 2017

This reprint edition: August 2026

ISBN-13: 978-93-5275-289-8

Printed at Shiv Shakti Printing and trading Co., Haryana

Contents

About the Book

"Nothing succeeds like success."
—Alexandre Dumas the Elder, 1854

And no other math resource helps kids succeed like Scholastic Great Math Practice! For classroom or at-home use, this exciting series for kids in grades 1 through 5 provides invaluable reinforcement and practice for math skills such as:

- ❑ number sense and concepts
- ❑ patterns, reasoning and logic
- ❑ basic operations and computations
- ❑ words problems
- ❑ time, money, and measurement
- ❑ fractions and decimals
- ❑ geometry and basic shapes
- ❑ graphs, charts, tables ... and more!

Each book contains loads of challenging puzzles, inviting games, and clever practice pages to keep kids delighted and excited as they strengthen their basic math skills.

What makes *Scholastic Great Math Practice* so solid?

- The chapters are aligned to the scope and progression of the NCERT syllabus. This ensures students are engaging with the worksheets in parallel to classroom lessons.

- Each practice page in the series reinforces a specific, age-appropriate skill as outlined by the NCERT.

- These skills give students the ability to interact with the mathematics they see and experience around them, fully meeting the objectives of the NCF.

Take the lead and help kids succeed with *Scholastic Great Math Practice*.
Parents and teachers agree: No one helps kids succeed like Scholastic!

Similar Halves

Name ______________________________ Date ______________

Tick the letters that have two similar mirror halves either or and draw the mirror-line.

A B C D E

G H I M O

P T U V W

X Y

Flying Through the Air

Name ______________________________ Date ______________

What is the last thing that the trapeze flier wants to be?

Find the symmetrical shapes (mirror halves). Then, use the Decoder to solve the riddle by filling in the blanks at the bottom of the page.

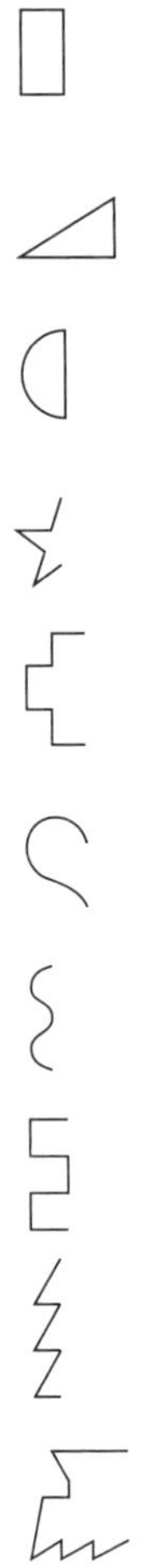

1 ______
2 ______
3 ______
4 ______
5 ______
6 ______
7 ______
8 ______
9 ______
10 ______

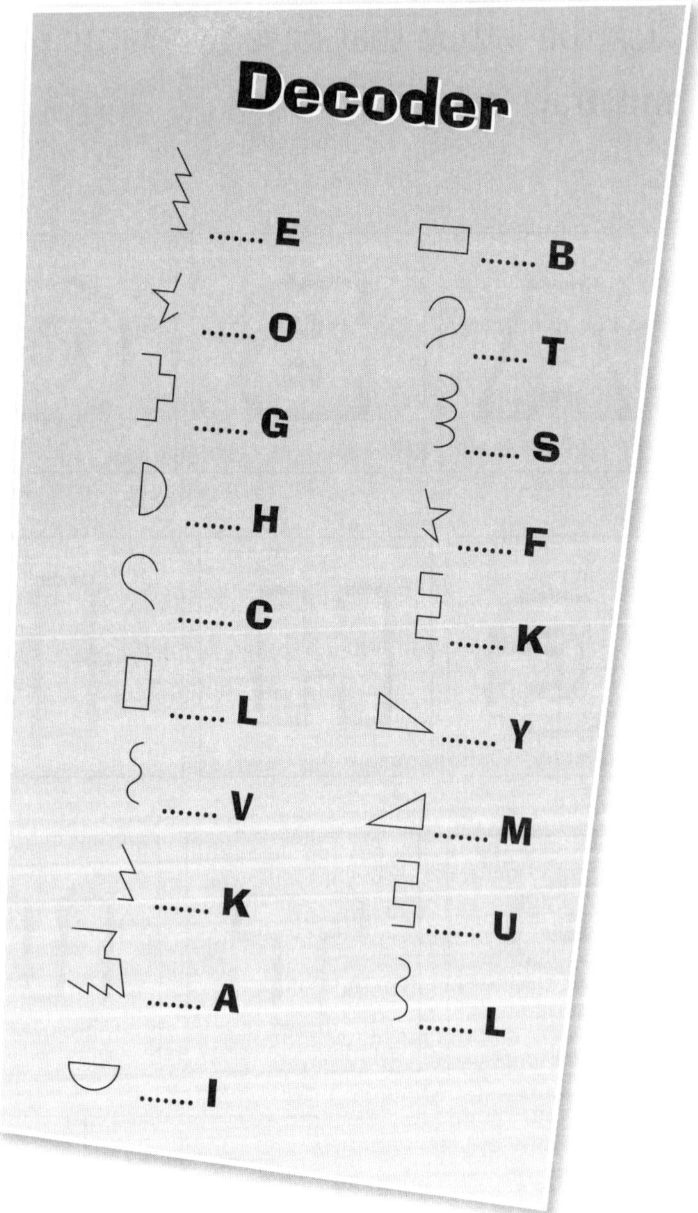

___ ___ ___   ___ ___ ___ ___   ___ ___ ___

6 3 9   4 10 1 7   5 8 2

Snowflakes on Mittens

Name ______________________________ Date ______________

Estimate how many snowflakes are on each mitten.
For the first mitten, skip count by 2s to find out.
(You can circle groups of 2.)
For the second mitten, skip count by 5s to check your answer.
(You can circle groups of 5.)

Extra

Would snowflakes really wait for you to count?
Explain your answer:

Riddle Fun

Name ______________________________ Date ______________

What wears shoes, sandals, and boots, but has no feet?

A ____ ____ ____ ____ ____ ____ ____ ____

To find out, write each number in standard form. Then, look for the numbers in the puzzle and circle them. They are written up, down, and backward. When you have circled all the numbers given, the letters in the blocks left uncircled spell the answer to the riddle. The first number has been circled for you.

4 B	**3** A	**2** R	**1** K	**9** S	**9** I	**5** G
8 R	**1** M	**7** Y	**1** S	**7** O	**5** D	**6** T
8 D	**5** W	**1** E	**8** T	**9** E	**1** S	**4** S
1 W	**6** P	**2** C	**5** X	**3** A	**3** Z	**9** P
4 L	**9** J	**7** F	**7** S	**0** R	**7** M	**0** L
8 H	**3** F	**6** Y	**9** K	**2** T	**0** E	**9** Q

8 ones, 1 ten, 5 hundreds = 518	**5 ones, 1 ten, 3 hundreds =** ☐	**6 ones, 7 tens, 2 hundreds =** ☐	**3 ones, 9 tens, 6 hundreds =** ☐
7 ones, 3 tens, 1 hundred = ☐	**4 ones, 6 tens, 5 hundreds =** ☐	**9 ones, 0 tens, 9 hundreds =** ☐	**1 one, 1 ten, 8 hundreds =** ☐
9 ones, 0 tens, 2 hundreds = ☐	**7 ones, 1 ten, 7 hundreds =** ☐	**6 ones, 3 tens, 8 hundreds =** ☐	**1 one, 2 tens, 3 hundreds =** ☐
8 ones, 8 tens, 4 hundreds = ☐	**7 ones, 5 tens, 8 hundreds =** ☐	**2 ones, 3 tens, 4 hundreds =** ☐	**7 ones, 0 tens, 7 hundreds =** ☐

Colorful Fish

Name ______________________________ Date ______________

Look at the numbers in the shapes inside the fish.

Use the information in the key at right to color the shapes.

If there is a . . .	Color the space . . .
6 in the tens place	green
5 in the hundreds place	blue
2 in the ones place	yellow
7 in the tens place	orange
9 in the hundreds place	red

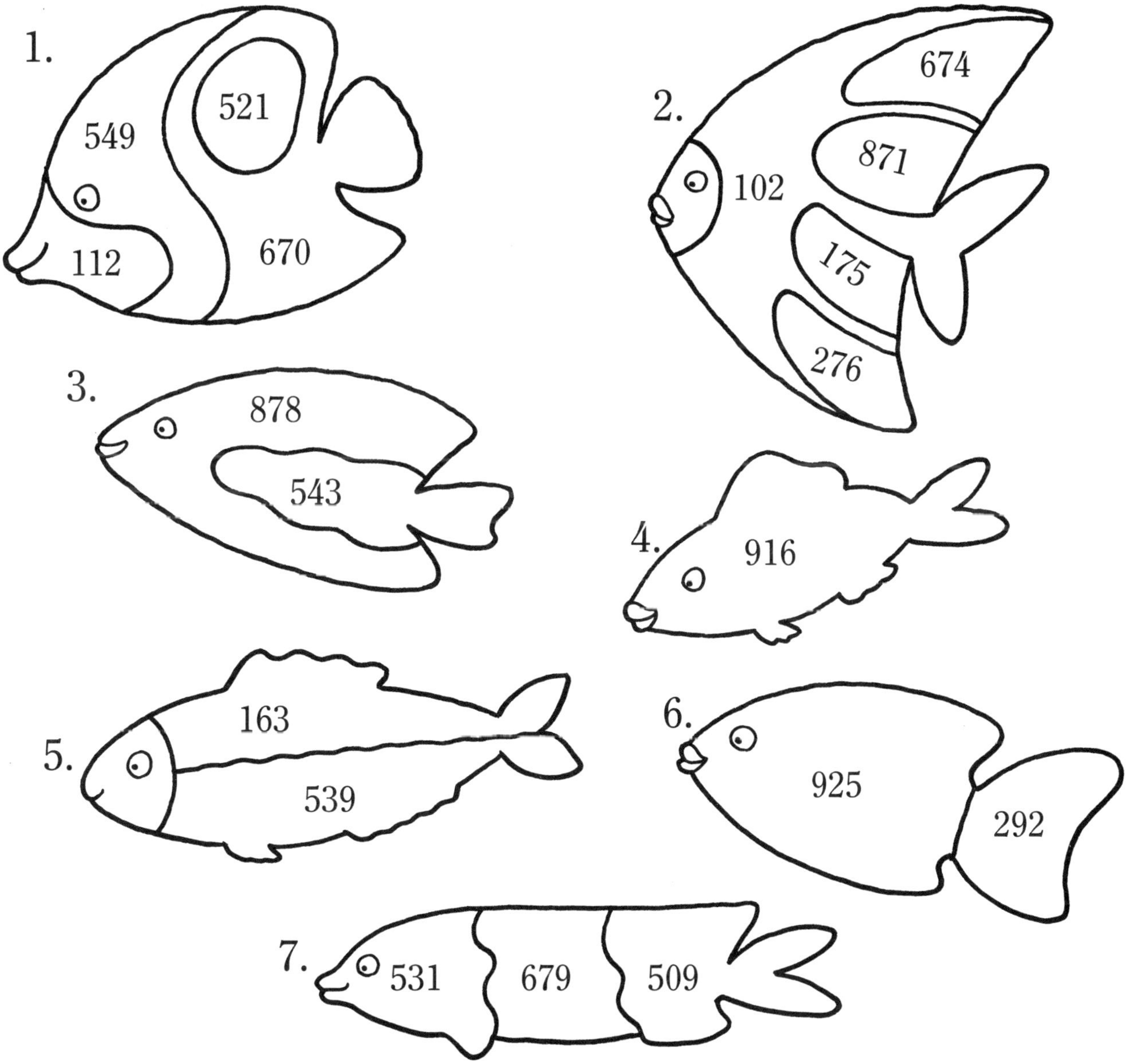

A Friendly Riddle

Name ______________________________ Date ______________

Riddle: When is the ocean friendliest?

Do each subtraction problem. Then, use the Decoder to solve the riddle by filling in the spaces at the bottom of the page.

1. 10 – 4 = __________
2. 19 – 16 = __________
3. 35 – 7 = __________
4. 27 – 19 = __________
5. 50 – 32 = __________
6. 84 – 47 = __________
7. 117 – 20 = __________
8. 155 – 144 = __________
9. 314 – 250 = __________
10. 572 – 86 = __________

Decoder

25	B
64	V
29	I
37	T
7	N
18	E
586	C
6	H
97	E
13	D
11	W
4	R
3	A
28	S
32	O
486	N
112	X
8	I
14	M

W ___ ___ ___   ___ ___   ___ ___ ___ ___ ___.
1 7 10   4 6   8 2 9 5 3

Tricky Twins

Name ______________________________ Date ______________

Sandy and Mandy are having a twin party. There are six sets of twins, but only one set of identical twins. To find the identical twins, solve the addition problems under each person. The identical twins have the same answer.

207 + 545

126 + 89

328 + 347

257 + 458

547 + 129

624 + 127

108 + 107

229 + 418

258 + 268

389 + 336

417 + 129

253 + 494

Clowning Around

Name ______________________________ Date ______________

At Arnold's Circus, all of the clowns dress alike. But there are really only two clowns that are exactly the same. Can you find them? Check your answer by solving the subtraction problem under each clown. The identical clowns have the same answer.

$$\begin{array}{r} 345 \\ -\ 186 \\ \hline \end{array}$$

$$\begin{array}{r} 879 \\ -\ 580 \\ \hline \end{array}$$

$$\begin{array}{r} 635 \\ -\ 241 \\ \hline \end{array}$$

$$\begin{array}{r} 977 \\ -\ 418 \\ \hline \end{array}$$

$$\begin{array}{r} 648 \\ -\ 109 \\ \hline \end{array}$$

$$\begin{array}{r} 492 \\ -\ 127 \\ \hline \end{array}$$

$$\begin{array}{r} 628 \\ -\ 329 \\ \hline \end{array}$$

$$\begin{array}{r} 863 \\ -\ 148 \\ \hline \end{array}$$

$$\begin{array}{r} 544 \\ -\ 261 \\ \hline \end{array}$$

$$\begin{array}{r} 860 \\ -\ 732 \\ \hline \end{array}$$

$$\begin{array}{r} 900 \\ -\ 119 \\ \hline \end{array}$$

$$\begin{array}{r} 969 \\ -\ 380 \\ \hline \end{array}$$

Plus & Minus Puzzle

Name ______________________________ Date ______________

In this crossnumber puzzle, your mission is to answer these addition and subtraction problems. So you don't get boxed in, we did the first one for you!

$$\begin{array}{r} 243 \\ -\ 126 \\ \hline 117 \end{array}$$

A 1	1	B 7	■	C	D
	■		■	E	
F		■	■	G	
■	■	H		■	
I	J		■	■	■
K		■	■	L	M
■	N		■	O	

ACROSS:

A. 243 – 126
C. 96 – 8
E. 76 – 9
F. 18 + 6
G. 81 – 52
H. 43 + 28
I. 234 + 323
K. 53 + 9
L. 84 – 16
N. 134 – 43
O. 80 – 46

DOWN:

A. 455 – 313
B. 41 + 34
C. 624 + 238
D. 260 + 8530
H. 169 – 92
I. 39 + 17
J. 600 – 71
L. 41 + 22
M. 65 + 19

SUPER CHALLENGE: Create your very own crossnumber puzzle. Make up your own addition and subtraction problems. Ask a classmate to complete your puzzle.

Curves Ahead!

Name ______________________________ Date ______________

How many centimetres long is each curved line? Guess. Then check by measuring.

1. My guess ______________

   Actual length ______________

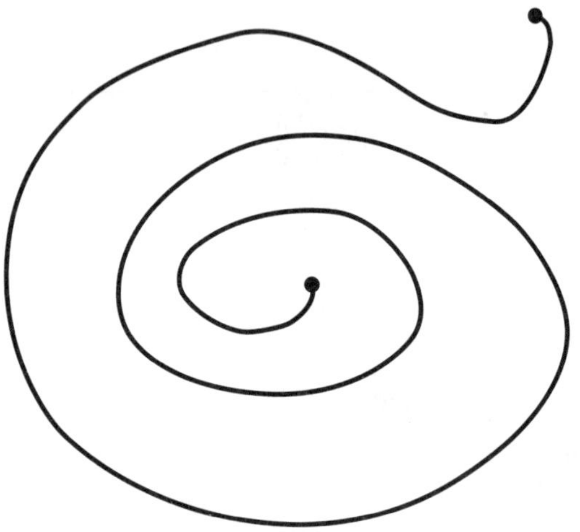

2. My guess ______________

   Actual length ______________

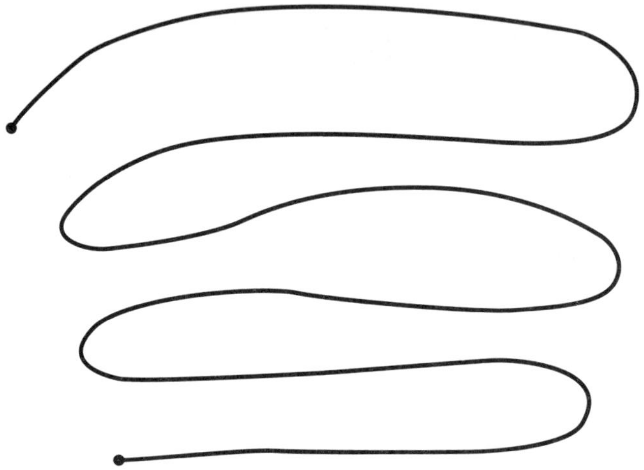

3. My guess ______________

   Actual length ______________

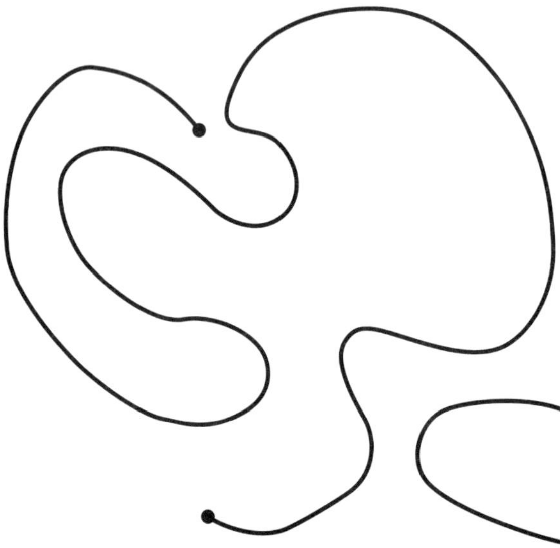

4. My guess ______________

   Actual length ______________

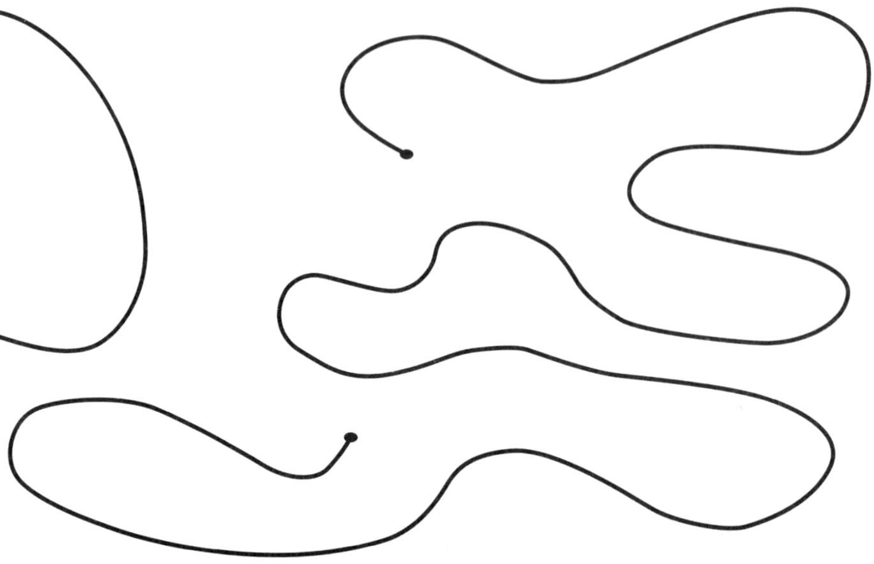

Measure With Me

Name ______________________________ Date ______________

Cut a piece of string or wool that is equal to your height. Measure each object below and check the correct box.

Object	Longer than my string	Shorter than my string	The same as my string

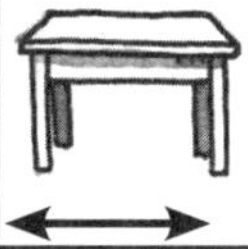			

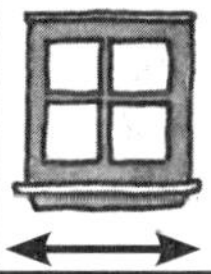			

- Measure something else. Draw a picture of it on another piece of paper. Write a sentence to show what you found out.

____

____

- Have someone measure you. Who measured you? ____________
How tall are you? ______________________________

Centimetres

Name ________________________________ Date ______________

Things can be measured using centimetres. Get a ruler that measures in centimetres. Measure the pictures of the objects below.

book  ______ centimetres	**book**  ______ centimetres
straw 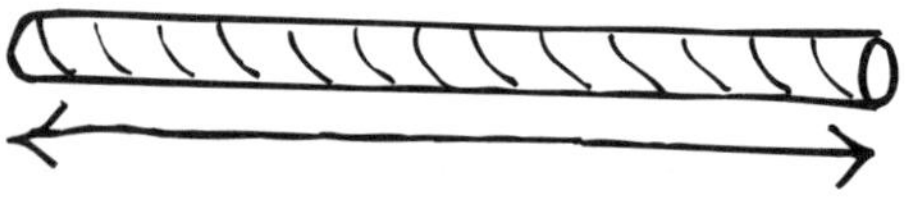 ______ centimetres	**marker** 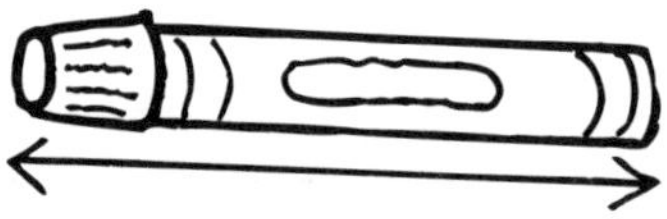 ______ centimetres
5 cubes 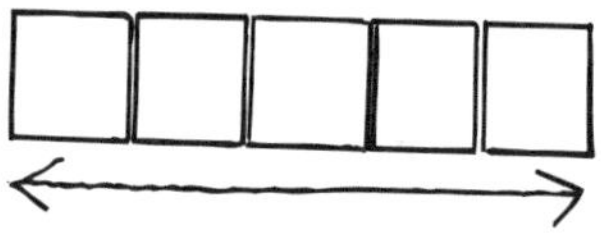 ______ centimetres	**10 cubes** 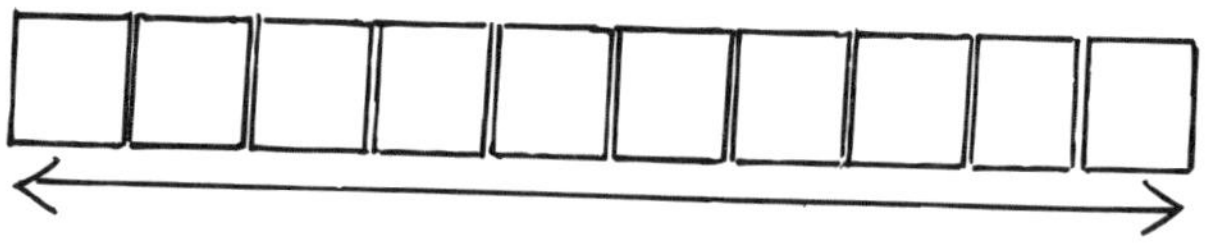 ______ centimetres
shoe 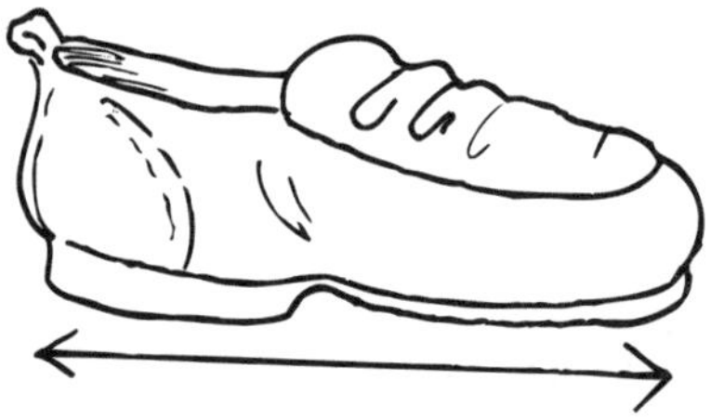 ______ centimetres	**hand** 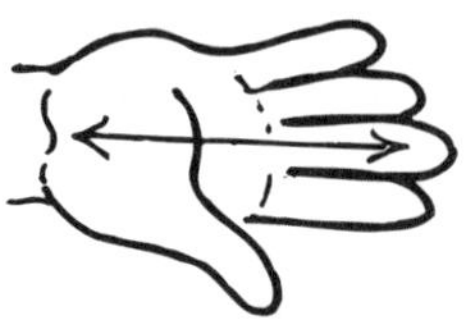 ______ centimetres

Penguin Family on Parade

Name ____________________ Date __________

The penguin family is part of the winter parade. They need to line up from shortest to tallest. Give them a hand! Use a ruler to measure each penguin. Label each penguin with its height. Then, write the name of each penguin in size order, from shortest to tallest.

Pavan	**Peter**	**Prashant**	**Parul**
Height:	Height:	Height:	Height:
______ cm	______ cm	______ cm	______ cm

Size Order:

__________ __________ __________ __________

(shortest) (tallest)

The Tree

Name ______________________________ Date ______________

Figure it out!

1. The apple that hit Rowena Pig fell from a branch that is 3 m above the ground. How far is the branch from the top of the 10m tree?

____

2. Rowena's ladder reaches up to 5 metres. How many metres shorter is the ladder than the 10-m tree? _______________________________

3. Starting on the ground, Itchy Squirrel climbs 2 metres up the tree. Then, she stops to rest. She climbs 7 metres more and stops to rest again. How many metres did Itchy climb up the tree? _______________________________

4. Rowena climbs 4 metres up the tree. Then, an apple falls on her. The apple fell from a branch that is 9 metres up the tree. How many metres did the apple drop before hitting Rowena? _______________________________

5. Itchy climbs 5 metres up the 10 metres tree. Then she climbs down 2 metres. How many metres is she from the top of the tree? _______________________________

SUPER CHALLENGE: Itchy is 2 metres from the top of the 10 metre tree. She jumps straight across to a second tree. Now she's 3 metres from the top of the second tree. How tall is the second tree? ______________

Pattern Block Design

Name ______________________ Date __________

How many total pieces are in this pattern block design?

2 + **2** + **1** = ______

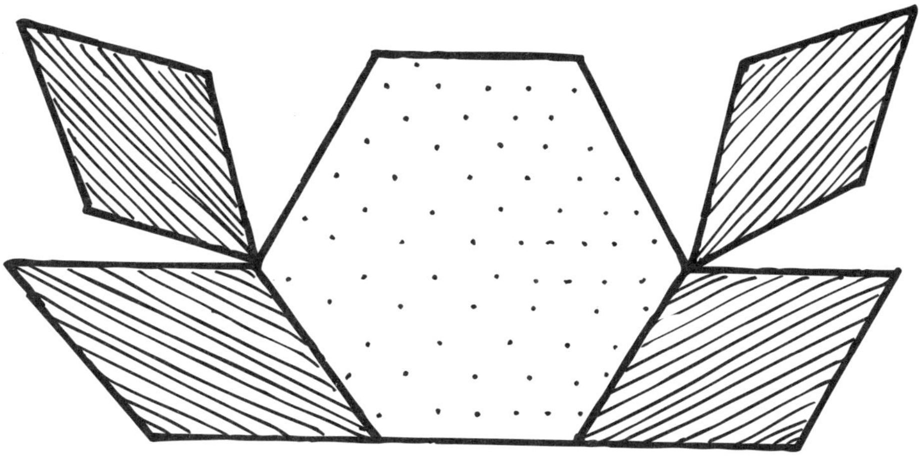

Now make your own design by drawing 5 pattern blocks. Connect the blocks to form a pattern different from the one above. You may want to use a block pattern more than once.

Write an equation to show how many of each shape you used.

Equation: ______________________________

Riddle Teller

Name ______________________ Date ____________

Read the riddle. Then, draw the shape it describes.

I have 3 sides and 3 corners. One of my corners is at the top.

1

I have no corners. One half of me is like the other half.

2

I have 4 corners and 4 sides. You can draw me by joining 2 triangles.

3

I have 5 sides and 5 corners. Draw a square and a triangle together.

4

I am not a square, but I have 4 sides and 4 corners.

5

I have 4 sides and 4 corners. My 2 opposite sides are slanted.

6

Don't Wait–Tessellate!

Name ______________________________ Date ______________

Find how easy it is to make beautiful tiled patterns.

Preparation

Mark and cut the cardboard into 8 cm by 8 cm squares.

Directions

Here are the steps in creating a tessellation.

1. Draw a simple shape on one side of the square. Some ideas:

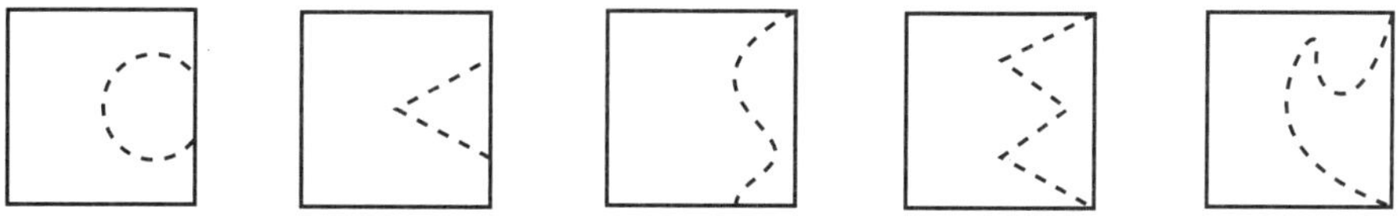

2. Cut out the shape, slide it directly to the opposite side of the square (don't turn it or flip it), and tape the straight sides together.

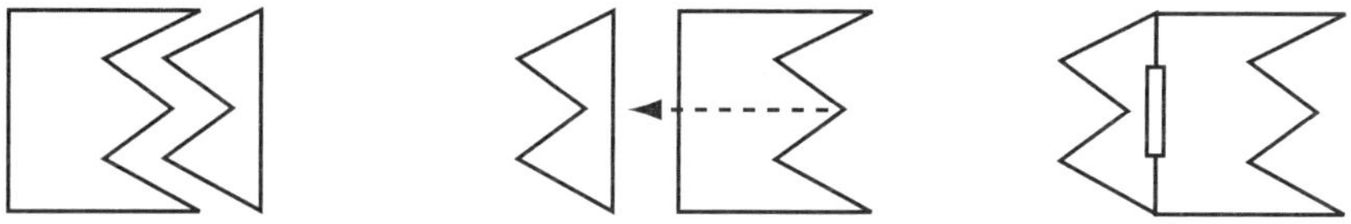

3. Repeat the process on one of the remaining sides. The tessellation template is complete.

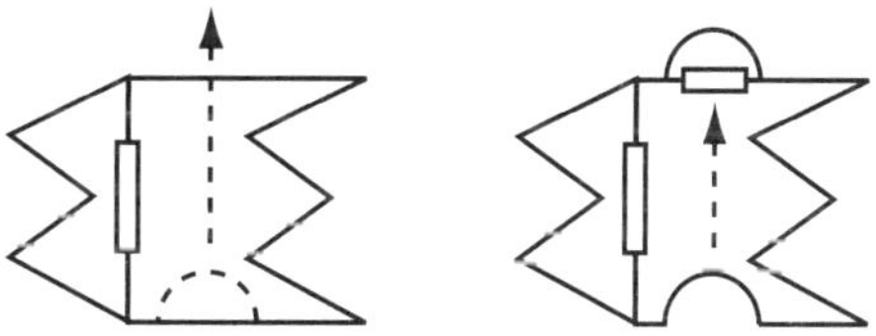

4. Trace the template in any spot on the construction paper. Slide the template in any direction (don't turn it or flip it), match the template with the first tracing, and trace it again. Repeat the process until the page is covered.

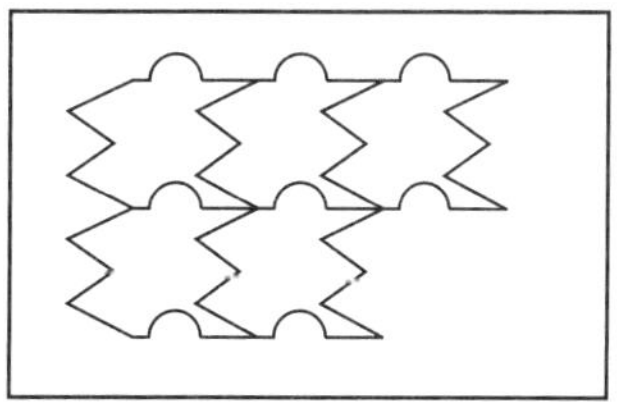

5. Colour the tessellation in any way. Decorate the shapes to bring out patterns of animals, people, flowers, or designs.

You'll Need

- Lightweight cardboard or oak tag
- Scissors and tape
- Crayons and construction paper (in a light shade)
- Pencils

Eager Leader

Name ______________________ Date ____________

	2	□	8
+	□	5	□
	6	7	9

	4	0	□
+	3	□	5
	□	1	8

	2	□	7
+	□	5	□
	3	9	8

	3	□	□
+	1	2	4
	□	7	8

	1	2	5
+	□	□	□
	4	7	9

	1	5	□
+	3	□	2
	□	9	2

	5	□	8
+	□	6	□
	7	6	9

	4	□	□
+	2	2	0
	□	7	9

	1	4	6
+	□	3	□
	3	□	8

	3	1	4
+	□	□	□
	4	3	7

Eager Achiever

Name ______________________________ Date ______________

	5		9
−		3	
	3	0	4

	5		5
−	4	6	8
		0	

	5		3
−		4	
	2	2	1

	9		
−	8	4	1
		4	3

	6	5	3
−		2	
	1		6

	3	3	
−	2		6
		0	3

		3	
−	4		7
		1	8

	7		
−	2	2	5
		4	3

		8	6
−	2	5	
	2		9

	8	5	0
−			
	5	2	6

Box of Many Colours

Name ______________________ Date ____________

Solve the problems. ◆ If the answer is between 0 and 200, colour the shape red. ◆ If the answer is between 201 and 400, colour the shape orange. ◆ If the answer is between 401 and 600, colour the shape yellow. ◆ If the answer is between 601 and 800, colour the shape blue. ◆ If the answer is between 801 and 999, colour the shape purple.

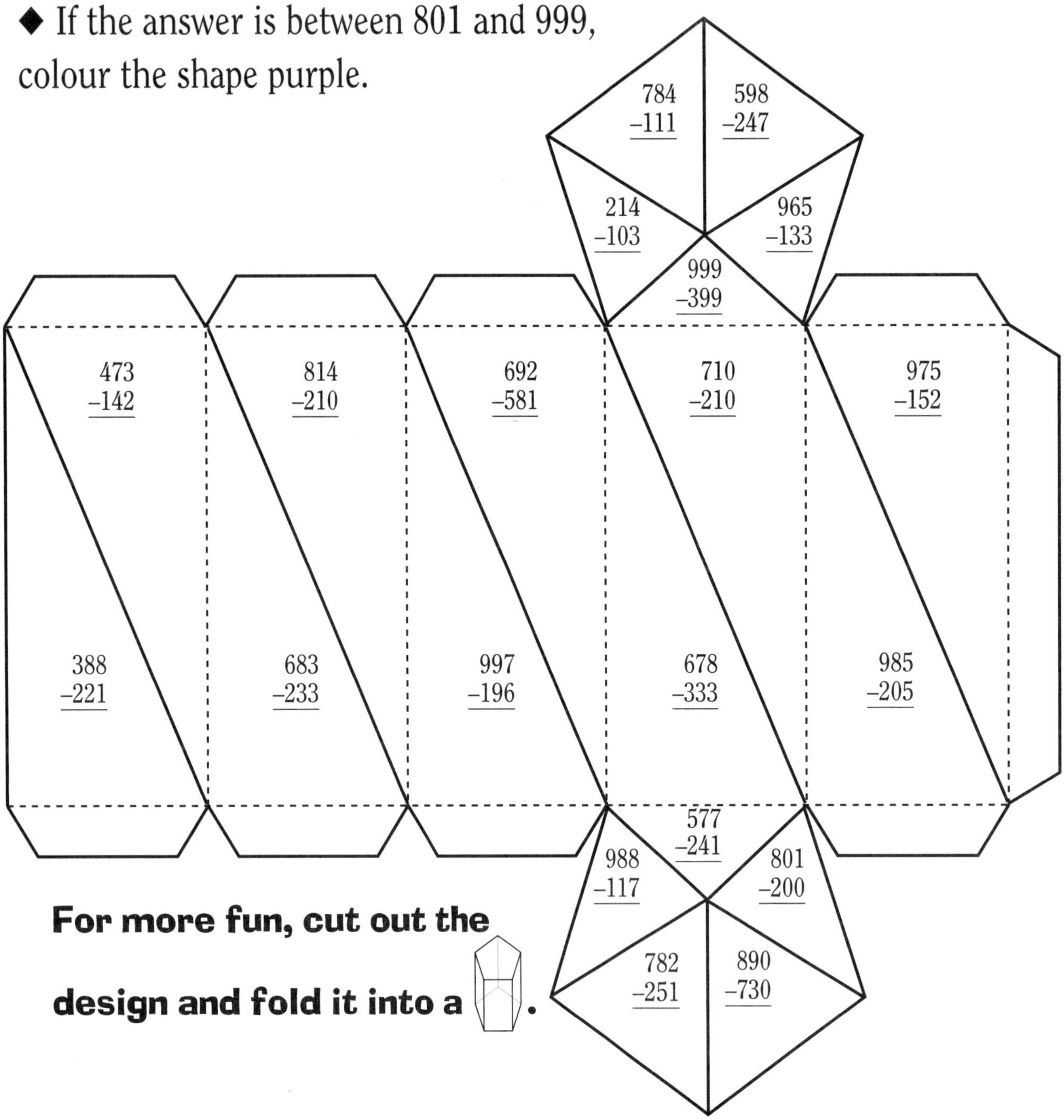

For more fun, cut out the design and fold it into a .

Gemstones

Name ______________________________ Date ______________

Solve the problems. ◆ If the answer is between 0 and 300, colour the shape red. ◆ If the answer is between 301 and 600, colour the shape green. ◆ If the answer is between 601 and 999, colour the shape yellow. ◆ Finish the design by colouring the other shapes with the colours of your choice.

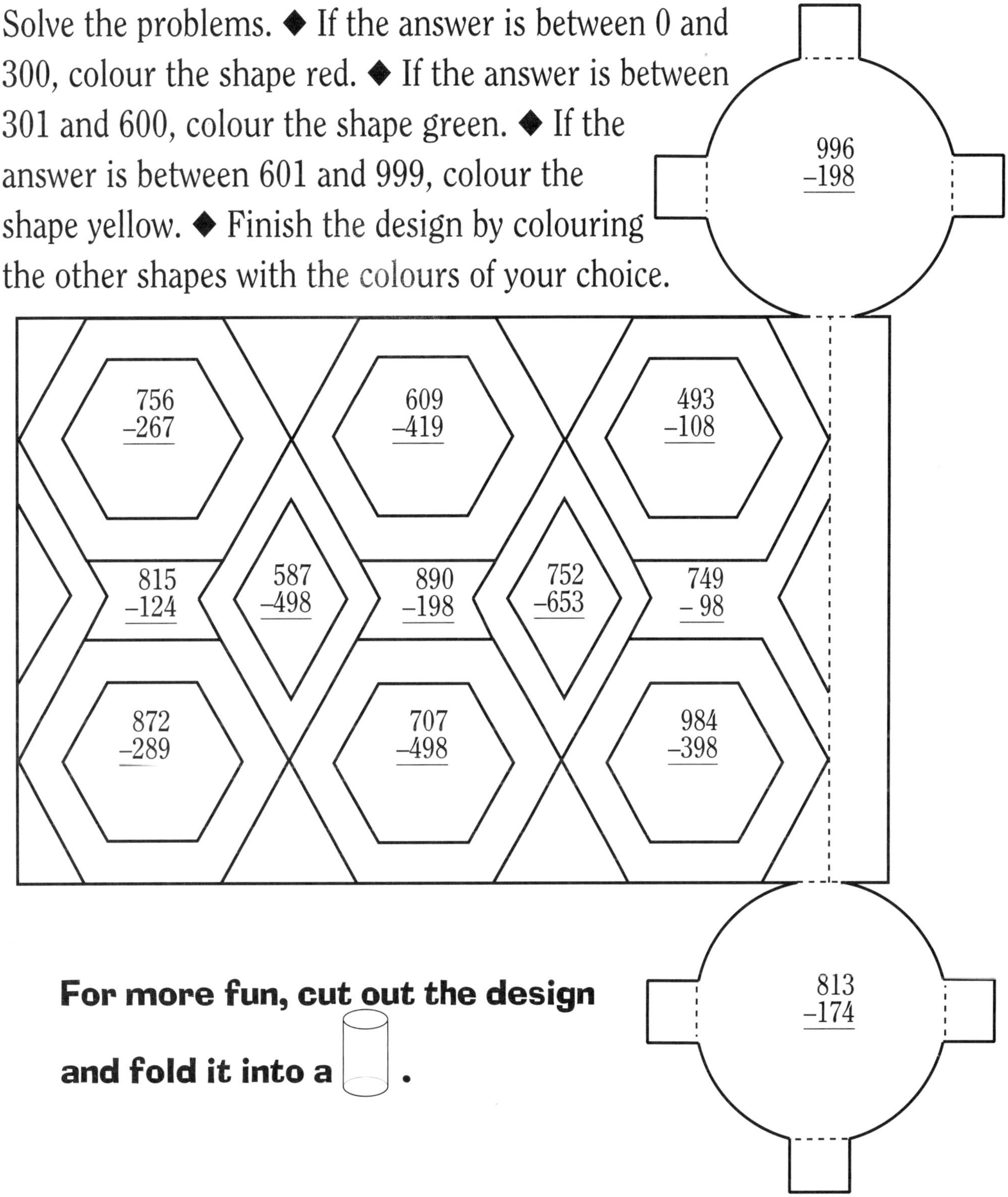

For more fun, cut out the design and fold it into a **.**

Clock Work

Name ______________________________ Date ______________

What's the time?

What's the time?

What's the time?

What's the time?

What do you do at 2:00 in the afternoon? Write about it on the lines below.

____

____

More Clock Work

Name ______________________________ Date ______________

Draw the hands on the clock so it shows 3:00.

Draw the hands on the clock so it shows 6:00.

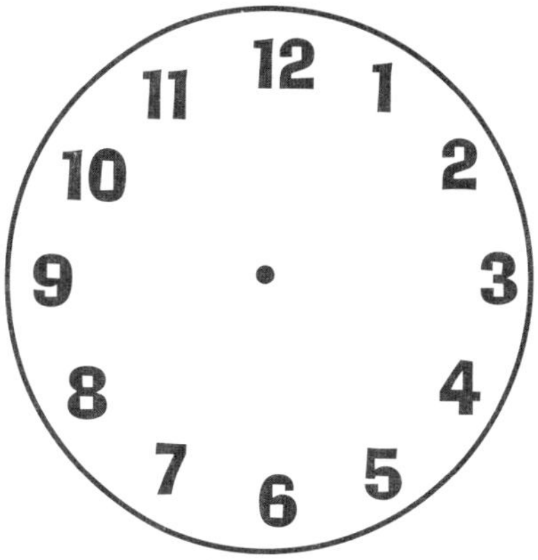

Draw the hands on the clock so it shows 9:00.

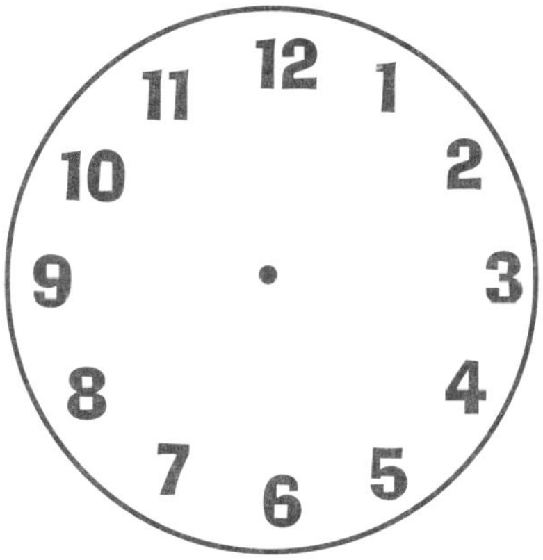

Draw the hands on the clock so it shows 12:00.

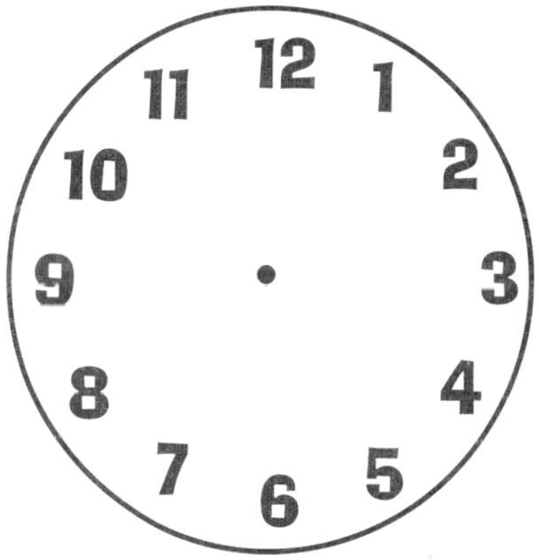

What do you do at 3:00 in the afternoon? Write about it on the lines below.

____

____

Telling Time

Name ______________________________ Date ______________

Write the time shown on each clock.

9. Write the times in order from earliest to latest, starting at 1:00.

______, ______, ______, ______, ______, ______, ______, ______

10. Draw the hands on each clock to show the time you do each activity.

I get up each morning at

I eat dinner at

I eat breakfast at

I go to bed at

Light and Heavy

Name ______________________________ Date ______________

From the word box below, choose the items (closest in weight) and write:

1. Two things heavier than a pen : ____________, ____________

2. Two things lighter than a pen : ____________, ____________

3. Two things heavier than a desk : ____________, ____________

4. Two things heavier than a 5 kg sack of wheat :

   ____________, ____________

5. Two things heavier than a 10 kg sack of cotton :

   ____________, ____________

6. One thing heavier than a car : ____________

car		chair	
tree	mobile phone		eraser
desk	pen		toothpick
	cup of tea		
10 kg sack of cotton	baby		5 kg sack of wheat

Going to Granny's

Name ____________________ Date ____________

Kelly is going to spend the night with her grandmother. She will need to take her nightgown, a shirt and some shorts. Into the suitcase go her toothbrush, toothpaste and hairbrush. Granny told her to bring a swimsuit in case it was warm enough to swim. Mom said to pack her favourite pillow and storybooks. Dad said, "Don't forget to take Granny's sunglasses that she left here last week." Now Kelly is ready to go!

Circle two items which you think are the lightest. Put a cross ✗ on the two items which you think are the heaviest.

SUPER CHALLENGE: On a separate sheet of paper, make a list of things you would pack if you were going to spend the night at your grandmother's house.

Heavenly Bodies

Name ______________________________ Date ______________

If these heavenly bodies were made of exactly the same material, then based on the size shown the diagram, order them from heaviest to lightest.

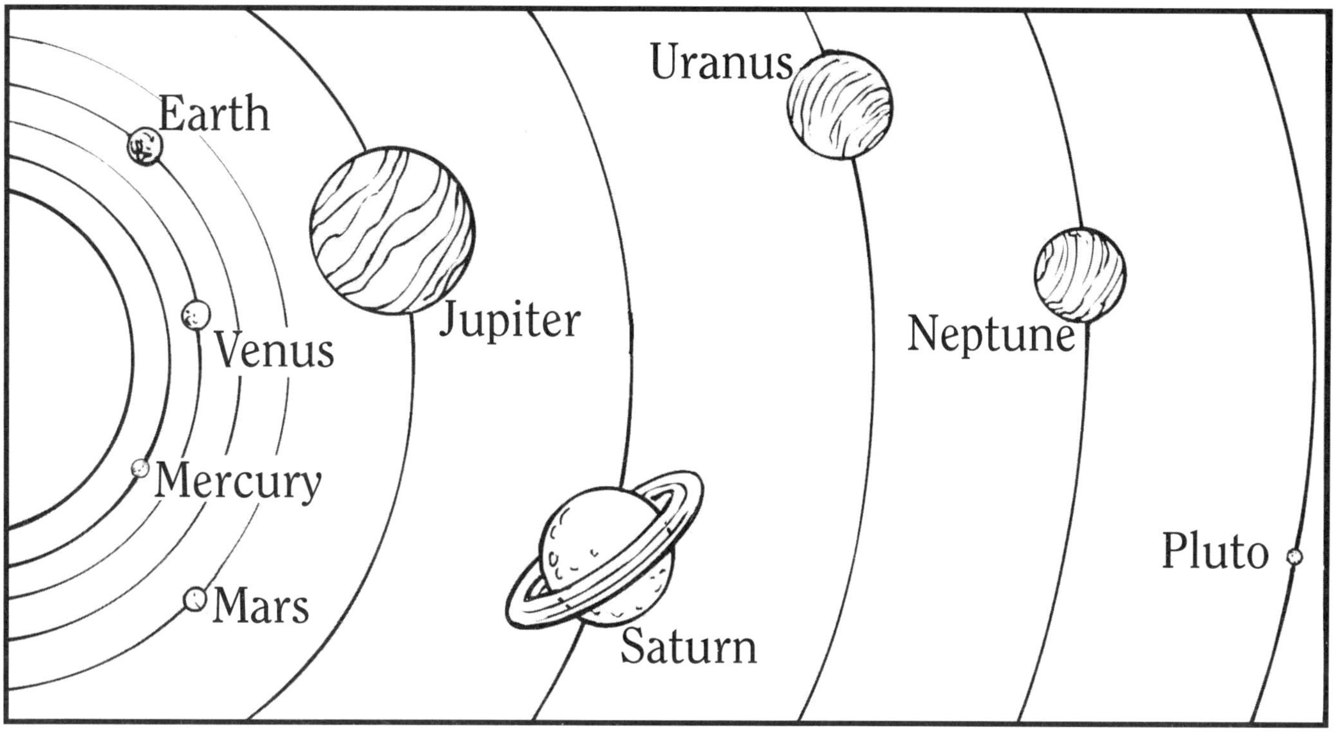

1. (Heaviest)______________________
2. ______________________
3. ______________________
4. ______________________
5. ______________________
6. ______________________
7. ______________________
8. (Lightest)______________________

Double It

Name ____________________ Date __________

These pots are all full of water. Draw a pot of the same shape that will weigh 'double' when full.

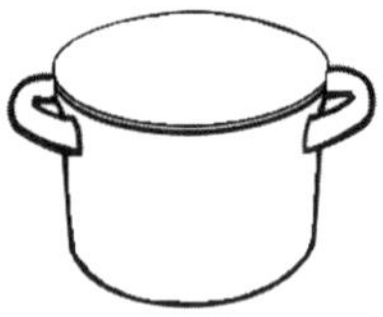

Time to Group

The multiplication symbol (x) can be thought of as meaning "groups of."

3 "groups of" 4 equals 12
3 x 4 = 12

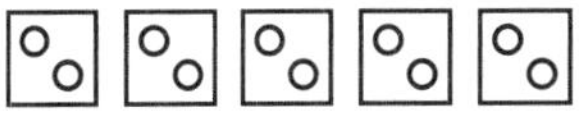

5 "groups of" 2 equals 10.
5 x 2 = 10

Write the multiplication sentence for each diagram.

A. 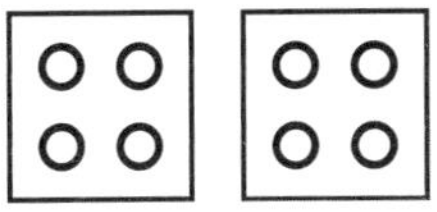

B. 

C. 

D. 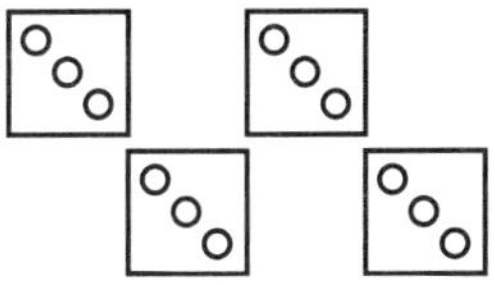

E. 

F. 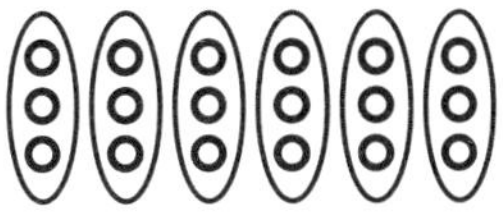

G. 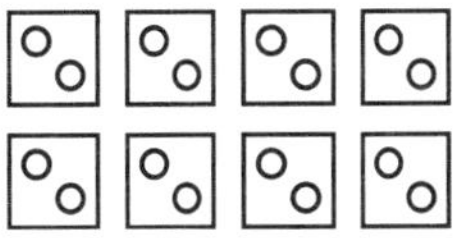

H. 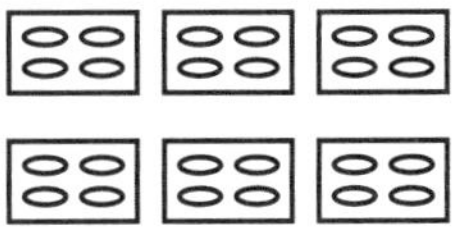

I. 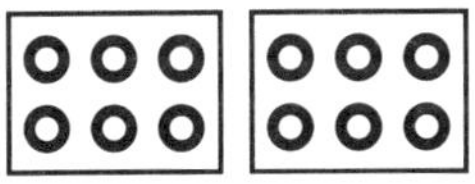

J. 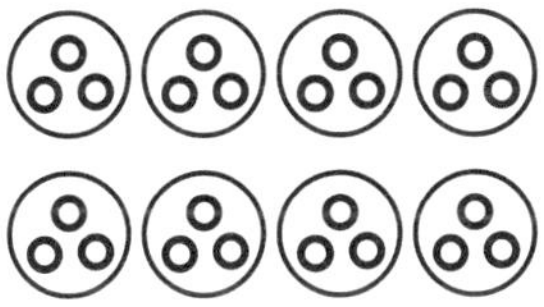

K. 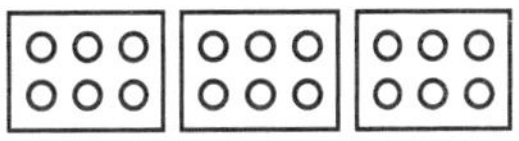

L. 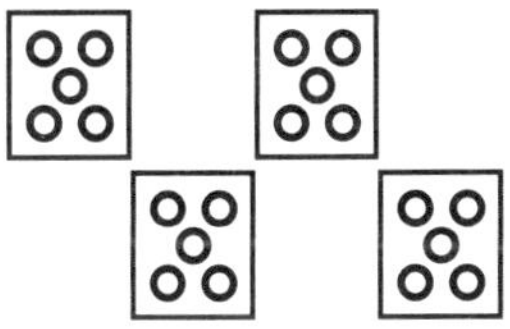

M. 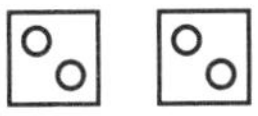

N. 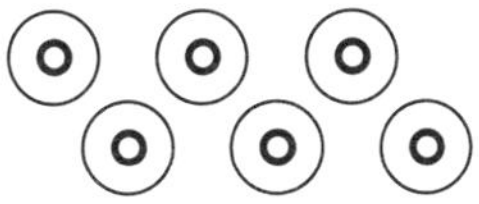

O. 

P. 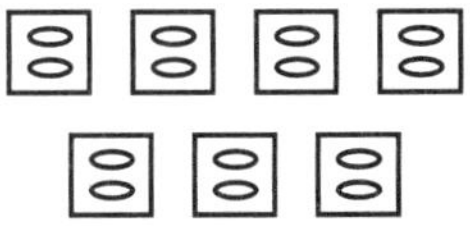

SUPER CHALLENGE: Divit has five bags of samosas. There are seven samosas in each bag. On another sheet of paper, draw pictures to show the total number of samosas.

Adding Quickly

The addition sentence 4 + 4 + 4 + 4 + 4 = 20 can be written as a multiplication sentence. Count how many times 4 is being added together. The answer is 5. So, 4 + 4 + 4 + 4 + 4 = 20 can be written as 5 x 4 = 20. Multiplication is a quick way to add.

Write a multiplication sentence for each addition sentence.

A. **5 + 5 + 5 = 15** __________

B. **6 + 6 + 6 + 6 = 24** __________

C. **8 + 8 = 16** __________

D. **2 + 2 + 2 + 2 = 8** __________

E. **7 + 7 + 7 = 21** __________

F. **4 + 4 + 4 + 4 = 16** __________

G. **9 + 9 + 9 = 27** __________

H. **5 + 5 + 5 + 5 + 5 = 25** __________

I. **3 + 3 + 3 + 3 + 3 = 15** __________

J. **10 + 10 + 10 + 10 = 40** __________

K. **1 + 1 + 1 + 1 + 1 = 5** __________

L. **11 + 11 + 11 = 33** __________

M. **8 + 8 + 8 + 8 = 32** __________

N. **0 + 0 + 0 + 0 = 0** __________

O. **12 + 12 + 12 + 12 = 48** __________

P. **9 + 9 + 9 + 9 = 36** __________

SUPER CHALLENGE: Today, we are going to the beach. Mom packed the picnic basket with six sandwiches, six water bottles, six candy bars, and six apples. How many items did she pack in all?

A Ray of Fun

An **array** demonstrates a multiplication sentence. The first **factor** tells how many rows there are. The second **factor** tells how many there are in each row. The answer of a multiplication sentence is called the **product**.

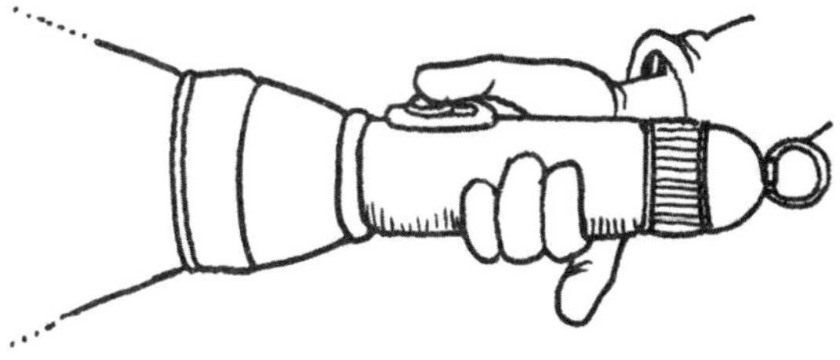

$2 \times 4 = 8$

○ ○ ○ ○ — 2 rows
○ ○ ○ ○ — 4 in each row

Write the multiplication sentence for each array.

A.
○ ○ ○
○ ○ ○
____

B.
○ ○ ○
○ ○ ○
○ ○ ○
____

C.
○ ○
○ ○
○ ○
○ ○
____

D.
○ ○ ○ ○ ○
○ ○ ○ ○ ○
○ ○ ○ ○ ○
____

E.
○ ○ ○
____

F.
○ ○ ○
○ ○ ○
○ ○ ○
○ ○ ○
____

G.
○ ○ ○ ○ ○ ○
○ ○ ○ ○ ○ ○
____

H.
○ ○ ○ ○
○ ○ ○ ○
○ ○ ○ ○
____

I.
○ ○ ○ ○ ○ ○
○ ○ ○ ○ ○ ○
○ ○ ○ ○ ○ ○
____

J.
○ ○ ○
○ ○ ○
○ ○ ○
○ ○ ○
○ ○ ○
____

K.
○
○
○
○
○
____

L.
○ ○
○ ○
○ ○
○ ○
○ ○
○ ○
○ ○
____

SUPER CHALLENGE: It was time for our family photo. The photographer arranged us into four rows. There were six people in each row. How many people in all were in the photo? On another sheet of paper, draw an array to solve this problem.

Picture-Perfect Star

Name ______________________________ Date ______________

Solve the problems. Then colour the design. Here's how: **1.** Choose four colours that you like. **2.** Write the name of one of the colours on each line below. **3.** Colour the puzzle. If the answer is between 1 and 200, colour the shape ___________. If the answer is between 201 and 500, colour the shape ___________. If the answer is between 501 and 700, colour the shape ___________. If the answer is between 701 and 900, colour the shape ___________.

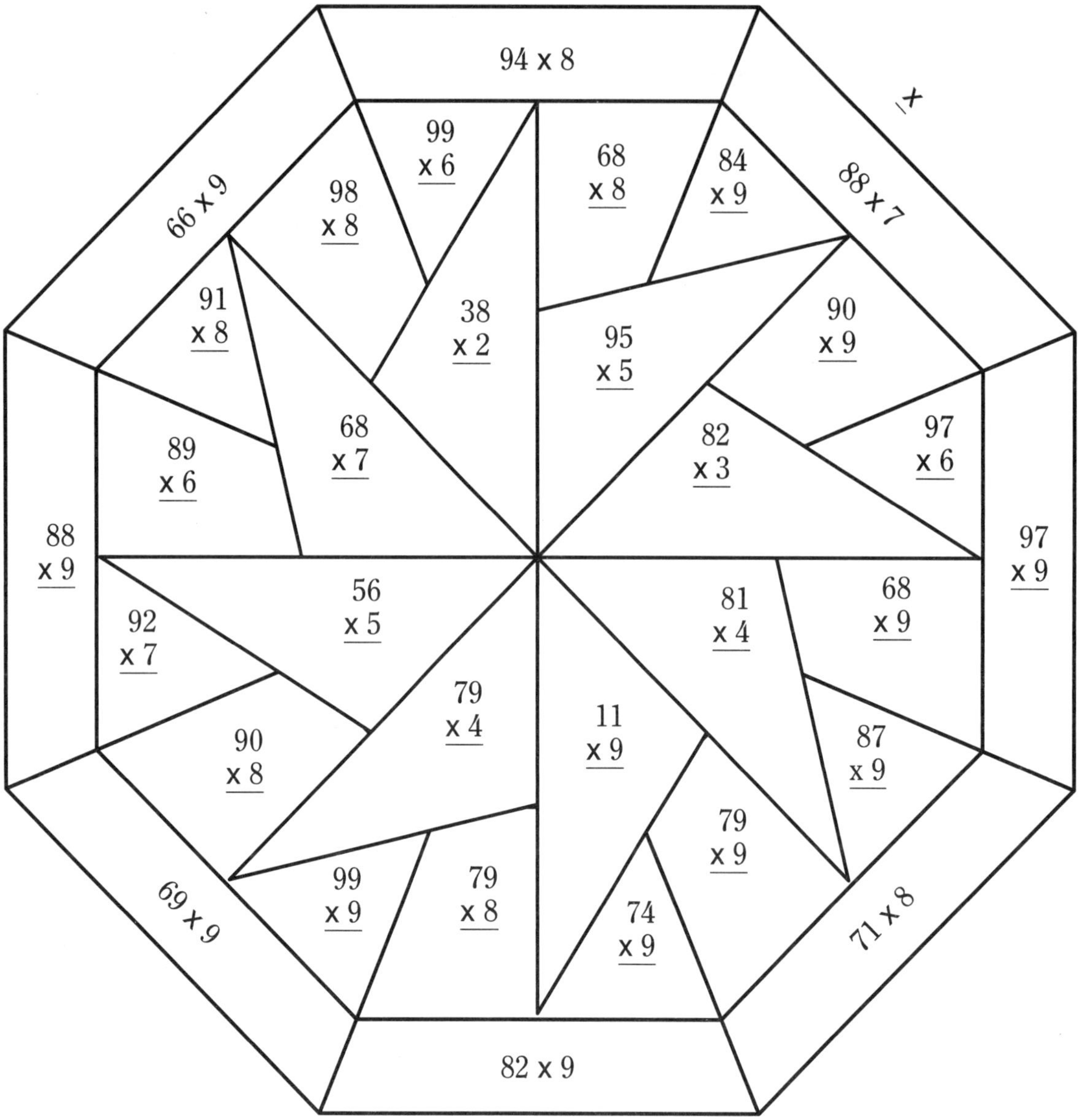

Taking It Further: Fill in the missing numbers.

a. 88 x ______ = 792 b. 56 x ______ = 392 c. 41 x ______ = 246

Soccer Balls

Name ______________________________ Date ______________

Solve the problems, then choose two colors that you like. ◆ Write the name of one of the colors on each line below. ◆ Color the design. If the answer is even, color the shape ________________. If the answer is odd, color the shape ________________. ◆ Finish the design by coloring the other shapes with the colors of your choice.

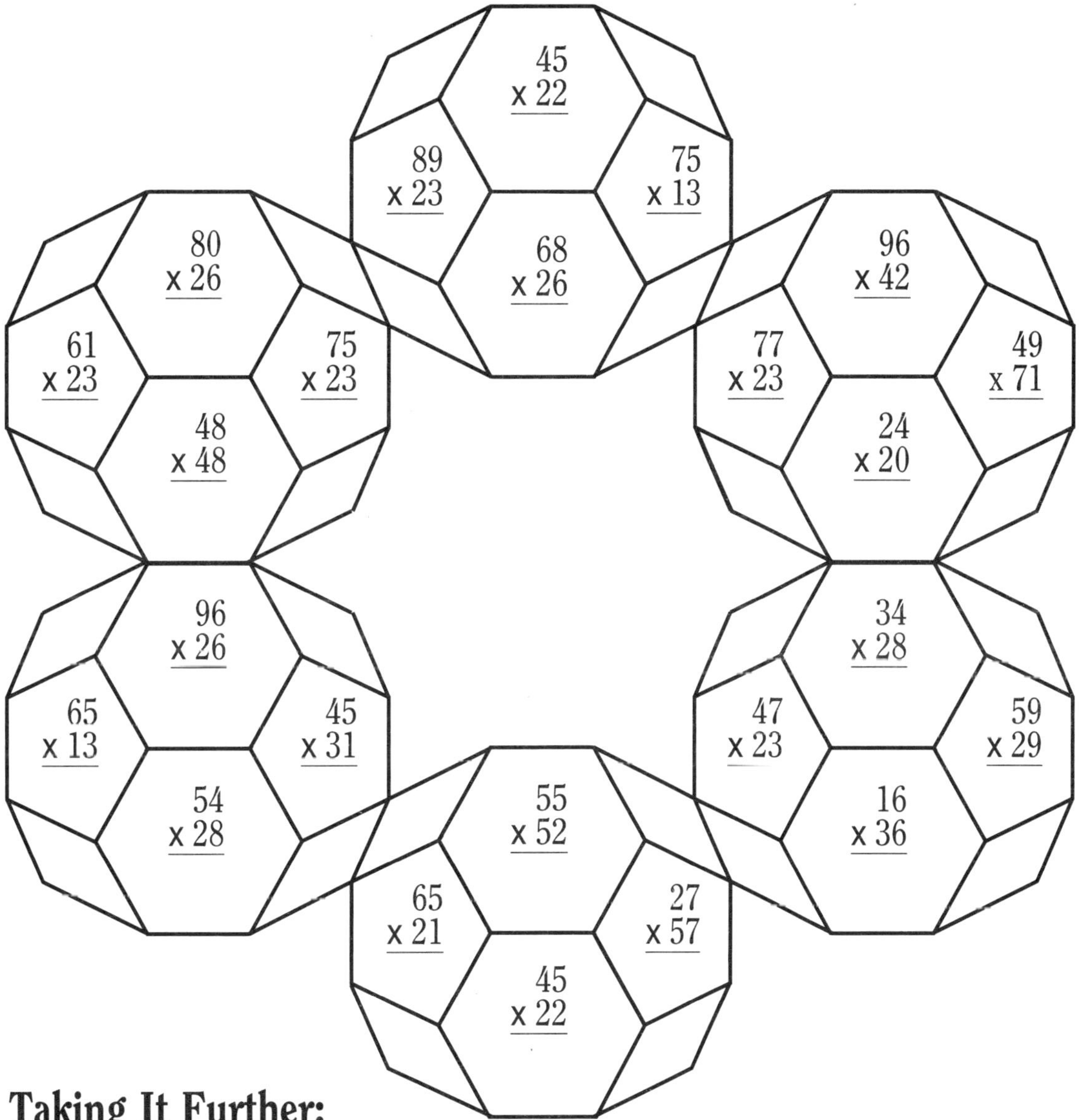

Taking It Further: Fill in the missing numbers.

a. 49 × 2☐ = 1,078

b. 78 × ☐9 = 1,482

c. 55 × 3☐ = 1,925

Who's Got the Button?

Name ______________________ Date ____________

Figure it out!

1. If a button is lost every 3 seconds, how many buttons are lost in 60 seconds? ____________

2. Ant Betty finds some buttons. She gives 7 buttons to each of her 8 nieces. How many buttons did she find? ____________

3. Molly Mouse organizes 6 groups of mice to look for lost buttons. Each group has 5 mice. How many mice are there in all? ____________

4. One group of mice finds many buttons and they put them into 9 bags. Each bag contains 14 buttons. How many buttons did the mice find? ____________

5. A second group of mice collects 20 bags containing a total of 160 buttons. Each bag contains the same number of buttons. How many buttons are in each bag? ____________

SUPER CHALLENGE: Suppose 20 mice want to form teams with an equal number of mice on each team. How many different-size teams can they form?

In the Wink of an Eye

Name ______________________________ Date ______________

Solve the problems. If the answer is even, connect the dot beside each problem to the heart on the right- and left-hand sides of the circle. If the answer is odd, do nothing. Two lines have been drawn for you.

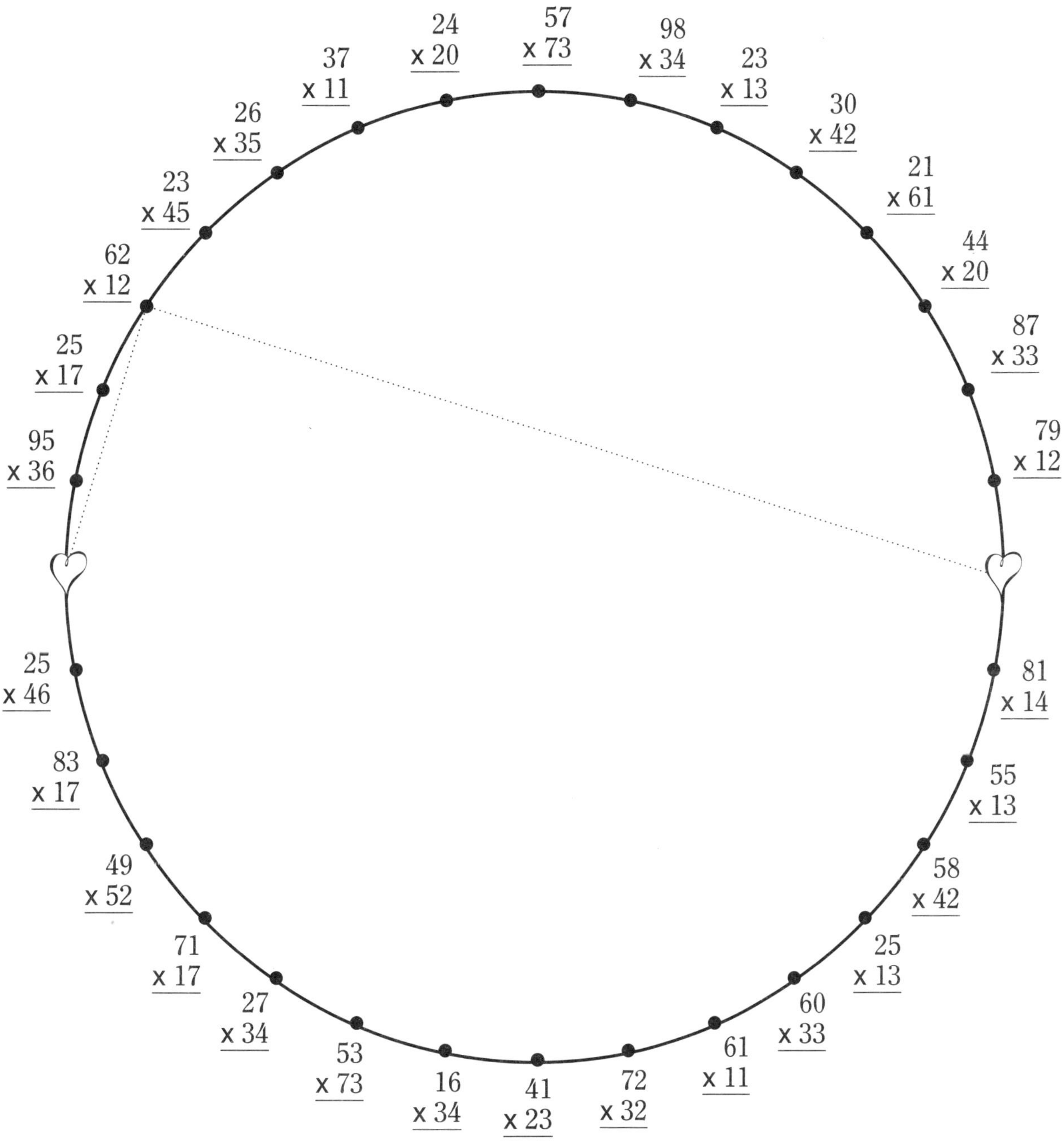

Missing Bone

Name ______________________________ Date ______________

McAllister the Mutt is dog-tired from walking in circles trying to find his bone. To help him find the path to the bone, move one paw print at a time in any direction, except diagonally. You can only follow the tracks that have odd numbers. Draw a line to show his route.

26	11	23	19	6	13		
12	5	36	9	3	7		
67	17	8	14	12	4	18	16
33	38	42	34	38	16	33	35
25	18			29	39	10	20
27	44	28	50	22	15	30	56
35	54	32	48	52	21	72	41
39	37	23	57	47	43	82	70
84	62	54	90	82	46	40	66

Pattern Learner

Name ______________________________ Date ______________

A pattern is a repeated arrangement of numbers, shapes, or lines in a row. Continue the patterns below.

1. 324, 435, 546,

2. 

3. 

4. 

5. 

6. 

7. A C E G I K

8. 11:05, 11:10, 11:15,

9. 

The Next Number . . .

Name ______________________________ Date ____________

Sometimes, sets of numbers have something in common. They follow a pattern. Take a look at the numbers 4, 6, 8, and 10. As the pattern continues, each number gets larger by 2. Try completing the number patterns in the problems below. Some are tougher to figure out than others. Give them a try. Good luck! Use the space below and to the right to work out the problems.

1. 8, 11, 14, 17, 20, _____, _____, _____

2. 27, 29, 31, 33, 35, _____, _____, _____

3. 2, 7, 12, 17, 22, 27, _____, _____, _____

4. 39, 46, 53, 60, 67, 74, _____, _____, _____

5. 4, 15, 26, 37, 48, _____, _____, _____

SUPER CHALLENGE: Come up with several number patterns of your own. Ask someone to complete the pattern.

Super Seven

Name ______________________________ Date ____________

How can you make the number seven even?

Find the answer by completing the next step in the pattern. Then, use the Decoder to solve the riddle by filling in the blanks at the bottom of the page.

1. 10, 7, 4, ___
2. 19, 13, 8, ___
3. 42, 40, 36, 30, ___
4. 56, 54, 50, 42, ___
5. 33, 32, 34, 33, 35, ___
6. 117, 97, 77, ___
7. 205, 175, 150, 130, ___
8. 344, 274, 214, 164, ___
9. 760, 660, 540, 400, 240, ___
10. 512, 490, 457, 413, 358, 292, ___

Decoder

5........................ **B**
1........................ **A**
97........................ **D**
215........................ **Y**
22........................ **W**
124........................ **H**
31........................ **I**
2........................ **P**
115........................ **A**
120........................ **C**
50........................ **N**
4........................ **E**
60........................ **S**
232........................ **M**
26........................ **T**
100........................ **R**
32........................ **F**
57........................ **E**
34........................ **K**

TA ___ ___   ___ ___ ___ ___   ___ ___ ___   “___”.

5 2   7 3 1 10   4 8 6   9

Can you hold me?

Name ______________________________ Date ______________

This shows a regular-sized glass of water .

Now keeping an eye on the glass, draw:

1. A jug that can hold five glasses of water.

2. A jug that can hold ten glasses of water.

3. A pot for making rice for five people.

4. A pot for making rice for ten people.

Fill it up

Name ______________________________ Date ______________

Sonya is pouring water from a standard-sized glass into jugs of different sizes. The pictures show the level of water after one glass of water is poured in each jug.

Tell how many glasses of water each jug can hold when full. You can draw lines in the jug. Then order the jugs from 1 to 4, 1 being the jug that can hold the most amount of water and 4 being the jug that holds the least.

A.  

B.  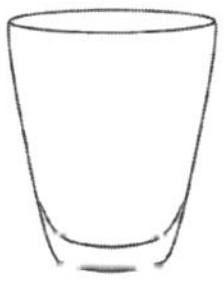

C.  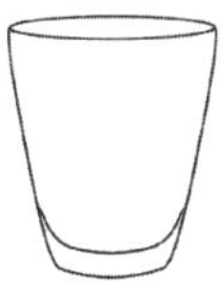

D.  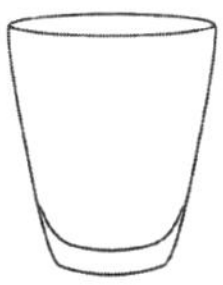

Eager Seeker

Name ______________________________ Date ______________

Divide the objects and food equally among the groups of people shown below. How many will each person receive? How much will be left over?

ITEM	NUMBER OF PEOPLE	EACH	LEFT OVER
1. 28 BALLS			
2. 15 SAMOSAS			
3. 8 ONE RUPEE NOTES			
4. 15 SLICES OF PIZZA			
5. 4 BALLOONS			
6. 25 CHOCHOLATES			
7. 6 TOY DINOSAURS			
8. 29 FRENCH FRIES			
9. 12 STRAWBERRIES			
10. 19 BISCUITS			

Candy Boxes

Name ______________________________ Date ______________

Sanjay works in a candy store. He puts candy into boxes. Each box has 10 spaces. Sanjay has 32 candies. Try to draw 32 candies in the boxes below. Write the number of candies in each box on the line. Write the number of any leftover candy at the bottom of the page.

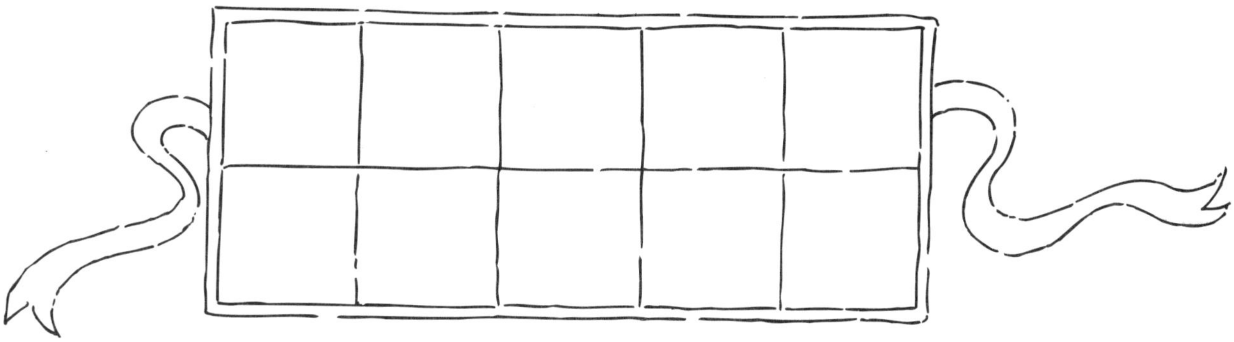

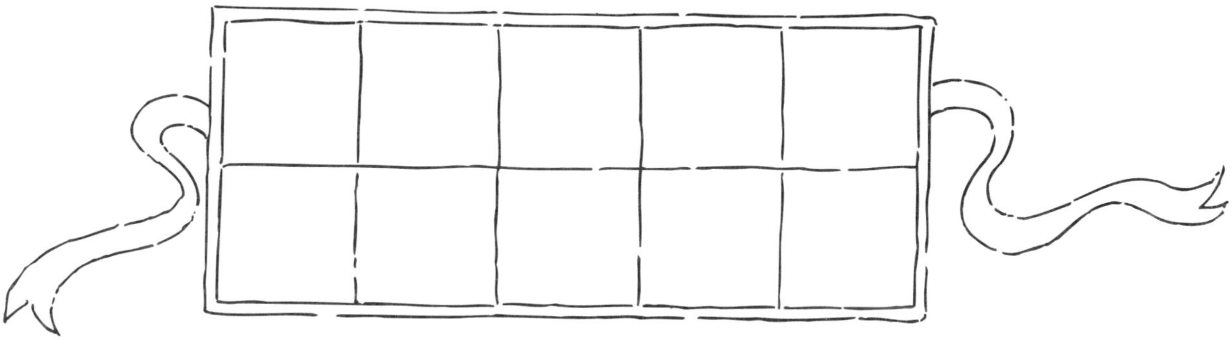

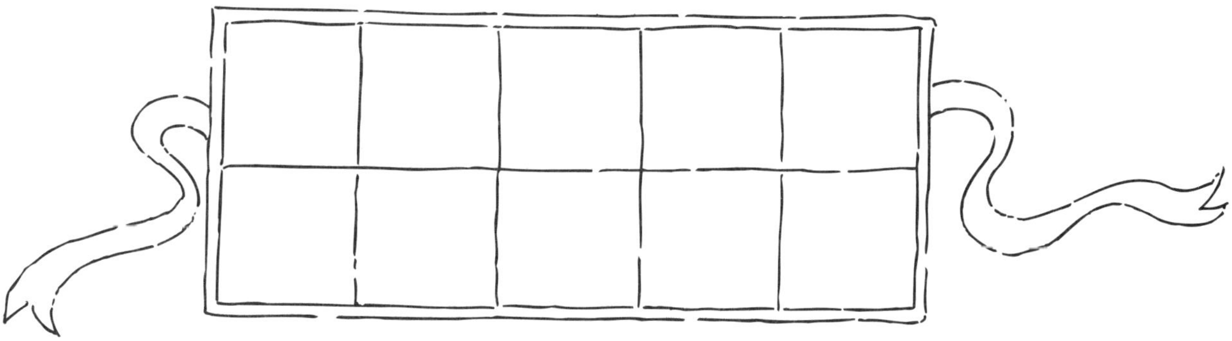

Extra

Leftover candies: ______________________________

Patchwork Diamonds

Name ______________________________ Date ______________

Solve the problems. ◆ If the answer is between 1 and 6, colour the shape green. ◆ If the answer is between 7 and 12, colour the shape red. ◆ Finish the design by colouring the other shapes with the colours of your choice.

Taking It Further: Jaya is making a quilt with 70 diamond-shaped pieces. If 7 pieces make 1 square, how many squares will her quilt have?

Football

Name ______________________________ Date ______________

Solve the problems. Then, connect the dot beside each problem on Line A to the dot beside its answer on Line B. One line has been drawn for you. Connect the dots beside each problem on Line C to the dot beside its answer on Line D.

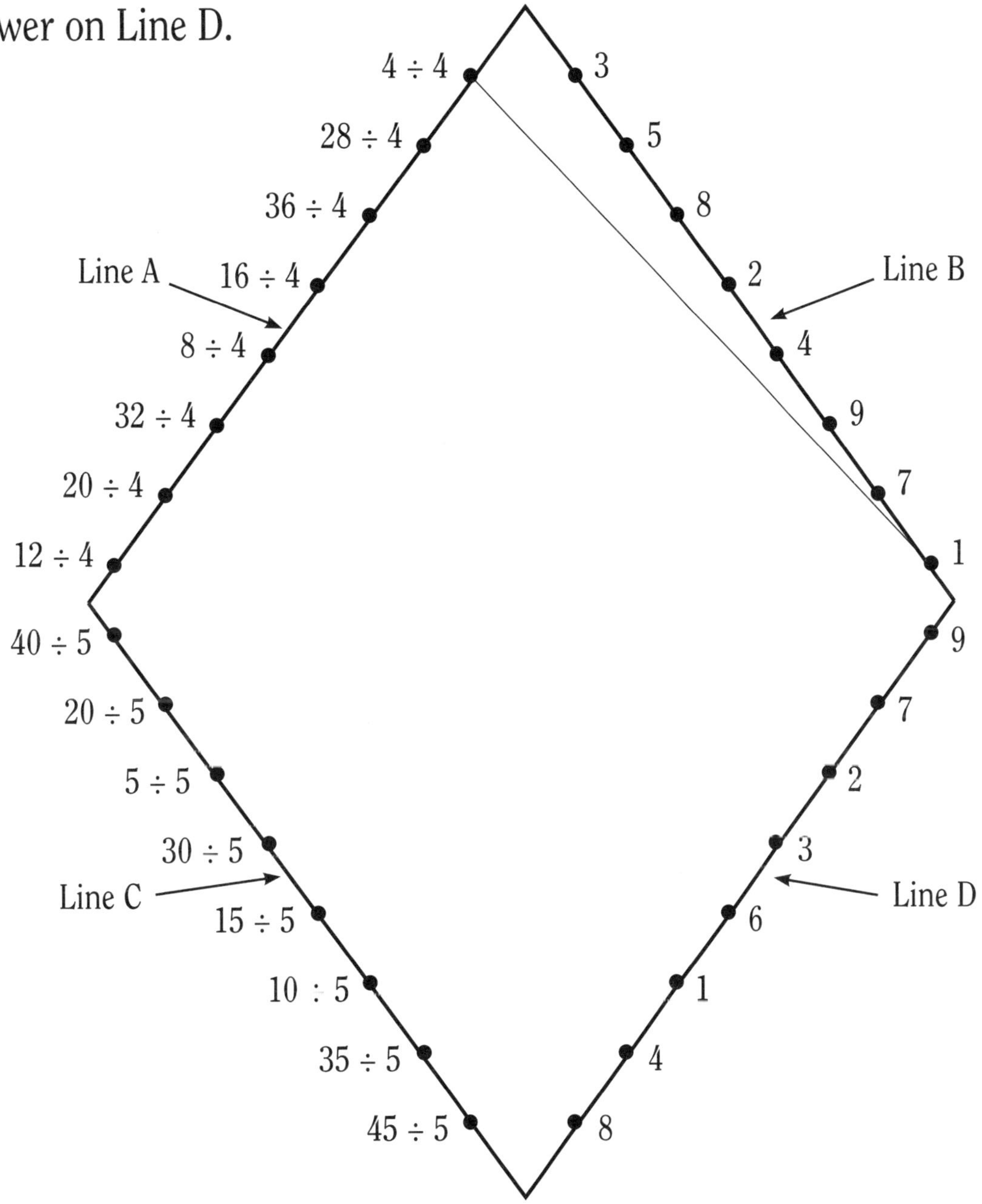

Taking It Further: There are 40 people in line at the museum. If they tour the museum in groups of 4, how many groups will there be?

Honeycomb

Name ______________________________ Date ______________

Solve the problems. ◆ If the answer has a remainder between 1 and 4, colour the shape black. ◆ If the answer has a remainder between 5 and 8, colour the shape red. ◆ Finish the design by colouring the other shapes with the colours of your choice.

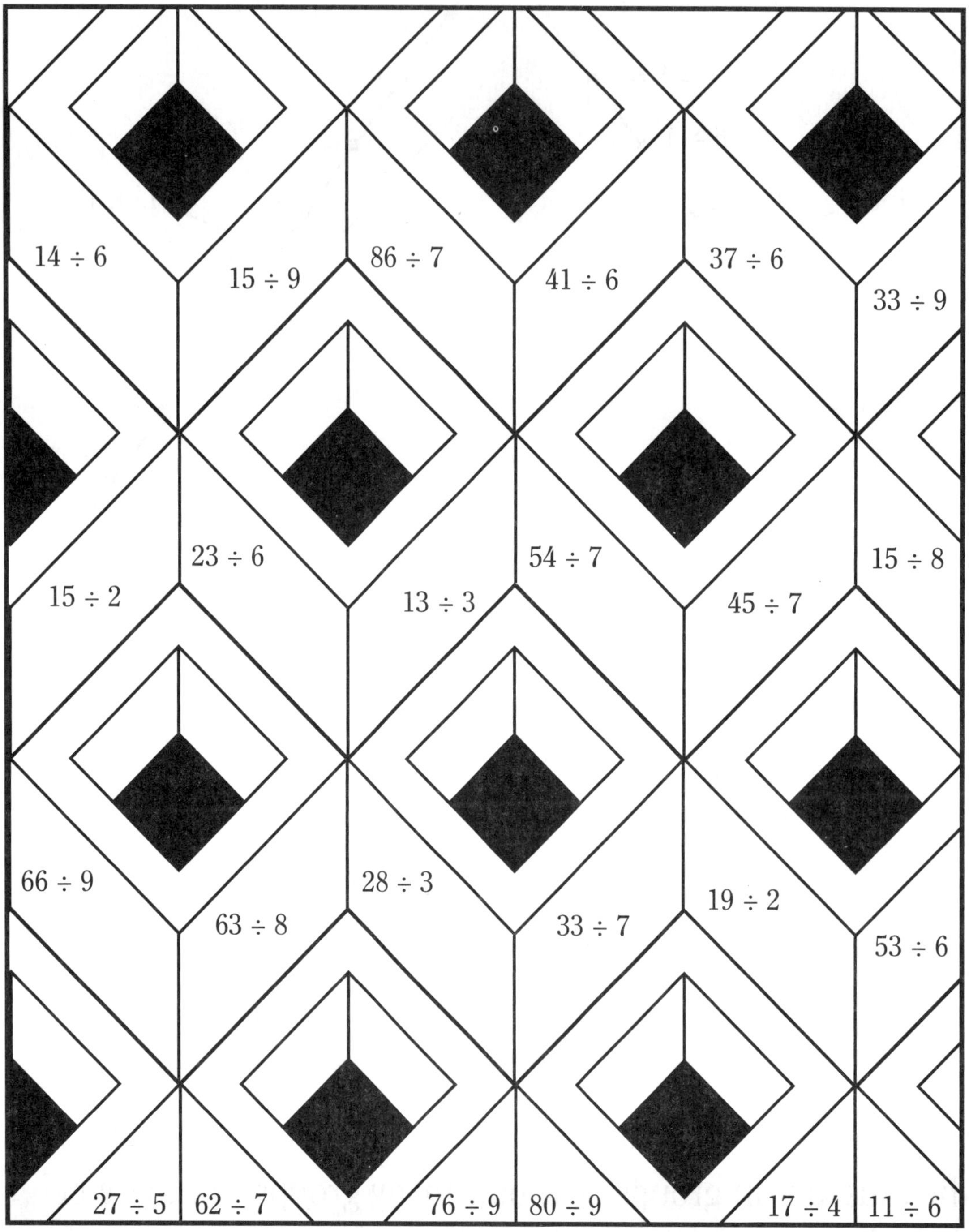

Five Senses

Name ______________________________ Date ______________

We learn about the world by using our 5 senses. The 5 senses are seeing, hearing, smelling, touching and tasting.

Look at the pictures on the left side of the graph. Think about which of your senses you use to learn about it. Draw a checkmark in the box to show the senses used. (Hint: You might use more than one.)

	See	**Hear**	**Smell**	**Touch**	**Taste**

Now graph how many senses you used for each object.

5					
4					
3					
2					
1					

Snuggle Up With a Book

Name ____________________ Date __________

Day of the Week	Reading Minutes
Sunday	97
Monday	28
Tuesday	73
Wednesday	44
Thursday	51
Friday	45
Saturday	80

Use the chart to answer the questions.

A. What day did Alex read for the longest time?

____

B. How many minutes did Alex read on Wednesday and Friday altogether?

_______ minutes

C. What day did Alex read for the shortest time?

____

D. How many more minutes did Alex read on Sunday than on Tuesday?

_______ minutes

E. How many minutes did Alex read on Monday and Thursday altogether?

_______ minutes

F. How many more minutes did Alex read on Tuesday than on Thursday?

_______ minutes

SUPER CHALLENGE: One hour is 60 minutes. On what days did Alex read longer than one hour?

__________, __________, __________

Great Graphing

Name ______________________________ Date ______________

The picture was made with 7 different shapes. How many of each shape was used? Colour in the shapes, following the instructions. Then colour in the boxes on the chart, 1 box for each shape used.

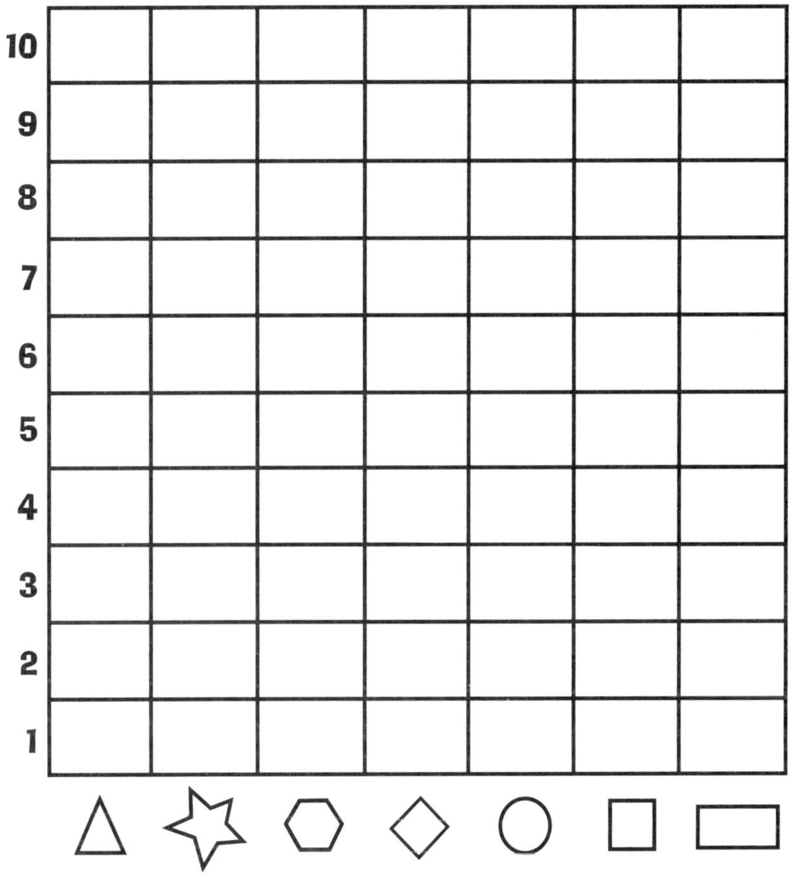

Colour the  red. Colour the  green. Colour the  blue.
Colour the  black. Colour the  orange. Colour the  yellow.
Colour the  purple.

Which shape was used the most? ______________________

Animal Caller

Name ______________________________ Date ______________

A bar graph shows information. This bar graph shows the speeds of animals in miles per hour (mph). A mile is a little more than $1\frac{1}{2}$ km. Use the graph to answer the questions.

WHICH ANIMAL IS...

1. THE FASTEST?

____

2. THE SLOWEST?

____

3. GOING 40 mph?

____

4. 20 mph FASTER THAN A CAT?

____

5. HOW MANY 4-FOOTED ANIMALS ARE LISTED?

____

DO THE BARS SHOW...

6. ANIMAL NAMES AND mph?

____

7. SPEED OR WEIGHT?

____

8. INFORMATION ABOUT TIGERS?

____

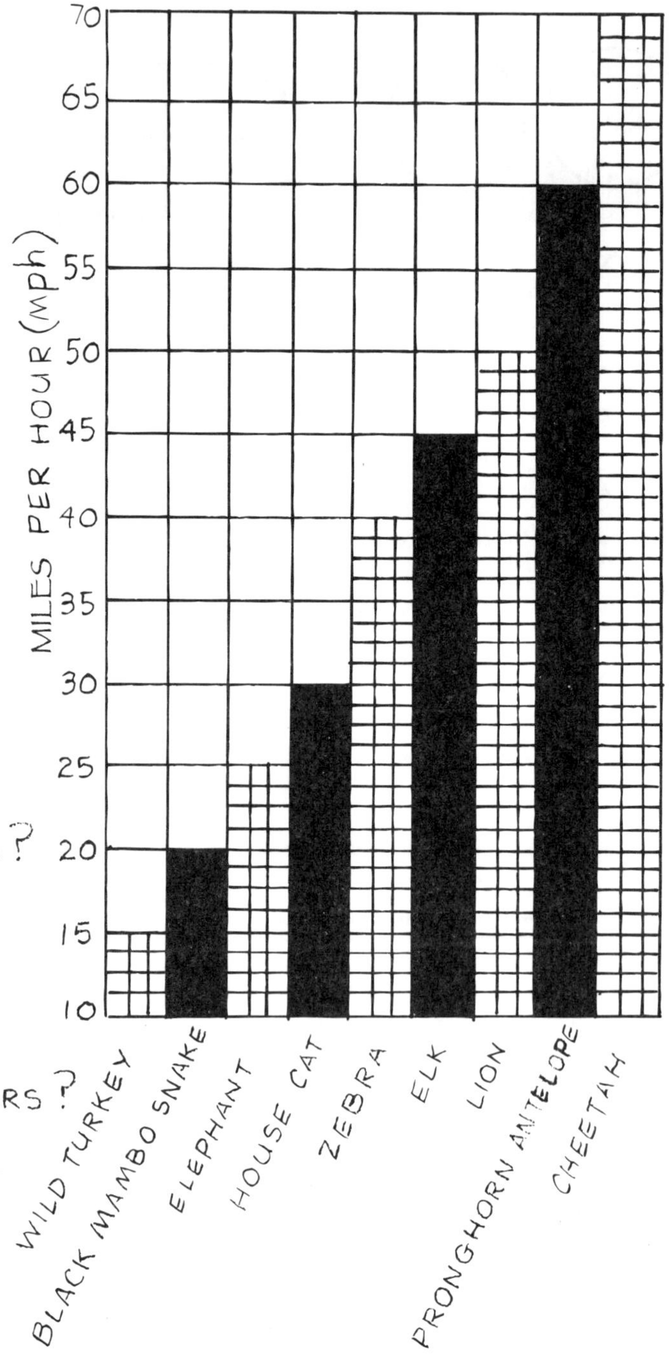

Patterns of Five

Name ____________________ Date __________

Look at the number chart below. Starting with 1, count 5 squares. Colour in the fifth square. Then, count 5 more squares and colour in the fifth square. Keep going until you reach 100.

Hundred's Chart

1	2	3	4	5	6	7	8	9	10
11	12	13	14	15	16	17	18	19	20
21	22	23	24	25	26	27	28	29	30
31	32	33	34	35	36	37	38	39	40
41	42	43	44	45	46	47	48	49	50
51	52	53	54	55	56	57	58	59	60
61	62	63	64	65	66	67	68	69	70
71	72	73	74	75	76	77	78	79	80
81	82	83	84	85	86	87	88	89	90
91	92	93	94	95	96	97	98	99	100

Tally marks can be arranged in groups of five, like this: 
Then you can count by fives.

Count how many girls and boys are in your class. Draw tally marks in groups of five.

Girls: ____________________ Boys: ____________________

Now, count the total number. Write the totals here:

Girls: ____________________ Boys: ____________________

Just Snacks

Name ______________________________ Date ____________

Use the menu on page 57 to answer the following questions.

1. Which snack costs the most?

   ____

   How much does it cost?

   ____

2. Which snack costs the least? ______________________________

   How much does it cost? ______________________________

3. Hamid spends ₹10 on two snacks.
   Which two snacks did he possibly buy? ______________________________

4. Gina has ₹15 and wants to buy a drink.
   Which drink can she order? ______________________________

5. Dhruv orders popcorn and a cookie.
   How much does he pay? ______________________________

6. Jai buys two cups of soup and a pack of salty crisps.
   How much does he spend? ______________________________

Small Snacks

Potato Chips .... ₹ 10

Salty Crisps .... ₹ 15

Popcorn .... ₹ 3

Peanuts .... ₹ 7

Puff .... ₹ 8

Teeny Sandwiches .... ₹ 4

Cup of Soup .... ₹ 2

Cookie .... ₹ 1

Pastry .... ₹ 15

Ice Cream .... ₹ 14

Cashews .... ₹ 9

Milk .... ₹ 20

Juice .... ₹ 12

Food to Go

Name ______________________________ Date ______________

Figure it out!

1. Woovis the Dog found a ₹5 note. Which item can he buy from the menu that will give the least change?

____

DOGGIE DINER BREAKFAST SHOP

MENU

Kibble	₹1.79
Mouse Crumbs	₹1.39
Table Scraps	₹2.49
Crumbs & Cheese	₹3.19
Deluxe Scraps	₹3.79

2. Woovis gets Crumbs & Cheese for breakfast. She pays with the ₹5 note. With the left-over money, what can Woovis buy to eat?

____

3. Which item can Woovis buy with the ₹5 note that will give the most change?

____

4. Which two items can Woovis buy with the ₹5 note so that he gets about ₹1 back in change?

____

5. Woovis ordered two items from the menu and gave the cashier the ₹5 note. But the two items cost more than ₹6.50. Which two items did Woovis order?

____

SUPER CHALLENGE: Can Woovis use the ₹5 Note to buy three different items from the menu? Why or why not?

Rupee Loopy

Name ____________________________ Date ______________

How many ways can you make twenty rupees? Write the number of coins you will need.

1.				
2.				
3.				
4.				
5.				
6				
7.				
8				
9.				
10.				
11.				
12.				
13.				
14.				
15.				

SHOW FOUR WAYS YOU CAN ₹ 63. YOU CAN USE EACH COIN MORE THAN ONCE

16. _____ _____ _____ _____

17. _____ _____ _____ _____

18. _____ _____ _____ _____

19. _____ _____ _____ _____

The Tooth About Money

Name ______________________________ Date ______________

Look at alligator's teeth.

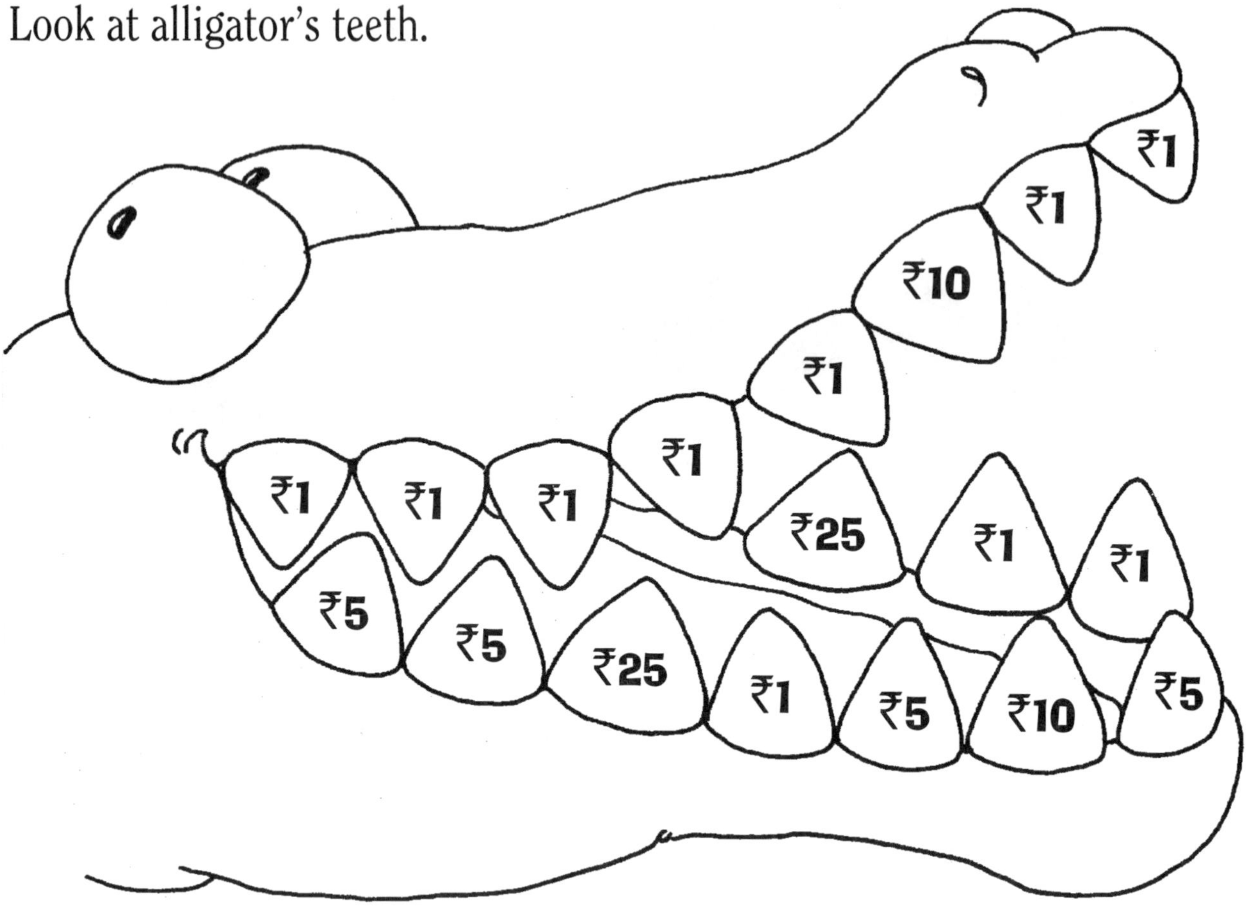

1. How many teeth have ₹1? ☐ ; Total value = ₹ __________

2. How many teeth have ₹5? ☐ ; Total value = ₹ __________

3. How many teeth have ₹10? ☐ ; Total value = ₹ __________

4. How many teeth have ₹25? ☐ ; Total value = ₹ __________

Answer Key

Page 5

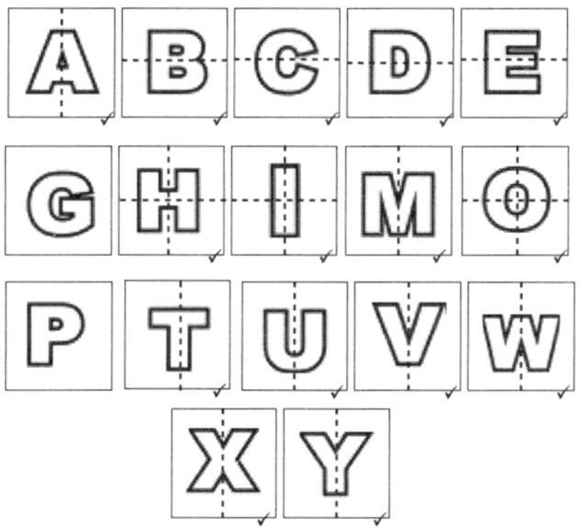

Page 6

1. 
2. 
3. 
4. 
5. 
6. 
7.
8. 
9. 
10. 

What is the last thing that the trapeze flier wants to be?
The fall guy

Page 7

Estimates will vary. 2, 4, 6, 8, 10, 12, 14, 16, 18, 20,
5, 10, 15, 20

Extra: No. Snowflakes would melt before you could count them.

Page 8

A sidewalk.
518, 315, 276, 693, 137, 564, 909, 811, 209, 717, 836, 321, 488, 857, 432, 707

4 B	3 A	2 R	1 K	9 S	9 I	5 G
8 R	1 M	7 Y	1 S	7 O	5 D	6 T
8 D	5 W	1 E	8 T	9 E	1 S	4 S
1 W	6 P	2 C	5 X	3 A	3 Z	9 P
4 L	9 J	7 F	7 S	0 R	7 M	0 L
8 H	3 F	6 Y	9 K	2 T	0 E	9 Q

Page 9

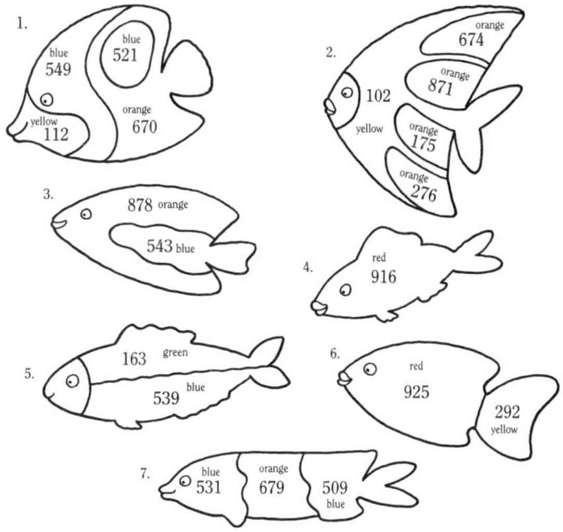

Page 10

1. 6; **2.** 3; **3.** 28; **4.** 8; **5.** 18
6. 37; **7.** 97; **8.** 11; **9.** 64; **10.** 486

When is the ocean friendliest?
When it waves

Page 11

207 + 545 = 752; 126 + 89 = 215;
328 + 347 = 675; 257 + 458 = 715;
547 + 129 = 676; 624 + 127 = 751;
108 + 107 = 215; 229 + 418 = 647;
258 + 268 = 526; 389 + 336 = 725;
417 + 129 = 546; 253 + 494 = 747

Page 12

345 – 186 = 159; 879 – 580 = 299; 635 – 241 = 394;
977 – 418 = 559; 648 – 109 = 539; 492 – 127 = 365;
628 – 329 = 299; 863 – 148 = 715; 544 – 261 = 283;
860 – 732 = 128; 900 – 119 = 781; 969 – 380 = 589

Page 13

A 1	1	B 7	■	C 8	D 8
4	■	5	■	E 6	7
F 2	4	■	■	G 2	9
■	■	H 7	1	■	0
I 5	J 5	7	■	■	■
K 6	2	■	■	L 6	M 8
■	N 9	1	■	O 3	4

Page 14

The actual measurements will vary somewhat, but they should be close to the following:

1. 37 cm
2. 48 cm
3. 34 cm
4. 53 cm

Pages 15

Answers will vary.

Page 16

2; $2\frac{1}{2}$; $3\frac{1}{2}$; $3\frac{1}{2}$; 7; 4; $2\frac{1}{2}$

Page 17

8 cm, 5 cm, 4 cm, 7 cm
Prashant, Peter, Parul, Pavan

Page 18

1. 7 m; **2.** 5 m; **3.** 9 m; **4.** 5 m; **5.** 7 m; **Super Challenge:** 11 m

Page 19

5
Children's patterns and sentences will vary.

Page 20

1. I HAVE 3 SIDES AND 3 CORNERS. ONE OF MY CORNERS IS AT THE TOP.

2. I HAVE NO CORNERS. ONE HALF OF ME IS LIKE THE OTHER HALF.

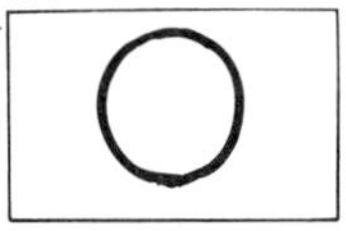

3. I HAVE 4 CORNERS AND 4 SIDES. YOU CAN DRAW ME BY JOINING 2 TRIANGLES.

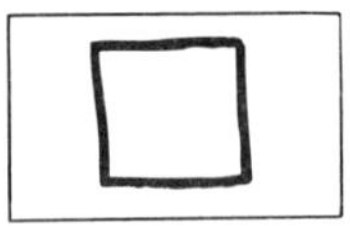

4. I HAVE 5 SIDES AND 5 CORNERS. DRAW A SQUARE AND A TRIANGLE TOGETHER.

5. I AM NOT A SQUARE BUT I HAVE 4 SIDES AND 4 CORNERS.

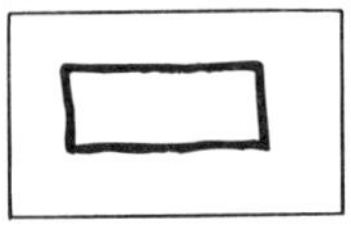

6. I HAVE 4 SIDES AND 4 CORNERS. MY 2 OPPOSITE SIDES ARE SLANTED.

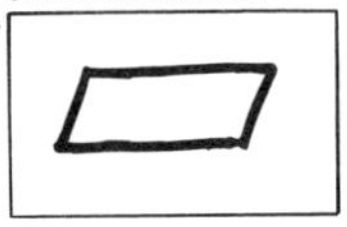

Page 21

Children's tessellate patterns will vary.

Page 22

228 + 451 = 679; 403 + 315 = 718
247 + 151 = 398; 354 + 124 = 478; 125 + 354 = 479
150 + 342 = 492; 508 + 261 = 769

459 + 220 = 679; 146 + 232 = 378; 314 + 123 = 437

Page 23

539 - 235 = 304; 575 - 468 = 107
563 - 342 = 221; 984 - 841 = 143; 653 - 527 = 126
339 - 236 = 103; 535 - 417 = 118

768 - 225 = 543; 486 - 257 = 229; 850 - 324 = 526

Page 24

784 - 111 = 673; 598 - 247 = 351; 214 - 103 = 111
965 - 133 = 832; 999 - 399 = 600; 473 - 142 = 331
814 - 210 = 604; 692 - 581 = 111; 710 - 210 = 500
975 - 152 = 823; 388 - 221 = 167; 683 - 233 = 450
997 - 196 = 801; 678 - 333 = 345; 985 - 205 = 780
577 - 241 = 336; 988 - 117 = 871; 801 - 200 = 601
782 - 251 = 531; 890 - 730 = 160

Page 25

996 - 198 = 798; 756 - 267 = 489; 609 - 419 = 190
493 - 108 = 385; 815 - 124 = 691; 587 - 498 = 89
890 - 198 = 692; 752 - 653 = 99; 749 - 98 = 651
872 - 289 = 583; 707 - 498 = 209; 984 - 398 = 586
813 - 174 = 639

Page 26

1. 4 o'clock, **2.** 8 o'clock, **3.** 10 o'clock, **4.** 9 o'clock
5. Answer will vary.

Page 27

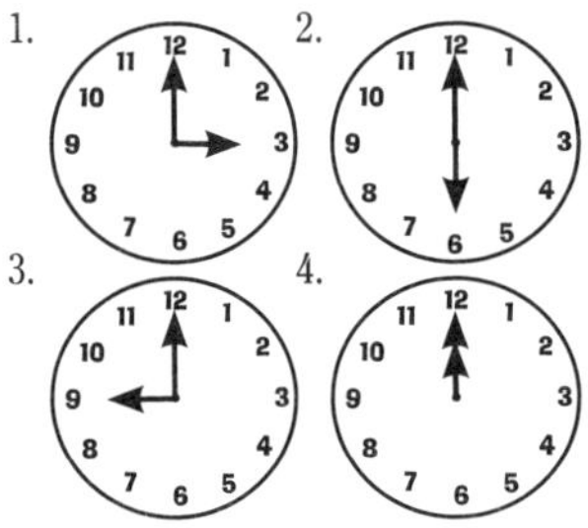

5. Answer will vary.

Page 28

Write the time shown on each clock on the line.

1. 3 : 0 0
2. 1 0 : 0 0
3. 2 : 0 0
4. 7 : 0 0
5. 5 : 0 0
6. 1 1 : 0 0
7. 1 : 0 0
8. 4 : 0 0

9. Write the times in order from earliest to latest, starting at 1:00.

1:00, 2:00, 3:00, 4:00, 5:00, 7:00, 10:00, 11:00

10. Answers will vary.

Page 29

1. car, tree, desk, 10kg sack of cotton, mobile phone, chair, 5 kg sack of wheat, cup of tea, baby
2. eraser (possibly), toothpick
3. car, tree, 10kg sack of cotton, 5 kg sackof wheat
4. car, tree, 10 kg sack of cotton
5. car, tree
6. tree

Page 30

Answers will vary, but check to make sure students can distinguish between 'heavy' and 'light' correcty.

Page 31

Jupiter, Saturn, Uranus, Neptune, Earth, Venus, Mars, Mercury, Pluto

Page 32

Drawing will vary, but check to make sure students can visualise and draw pots that are approximately two times bigger.

Page 33

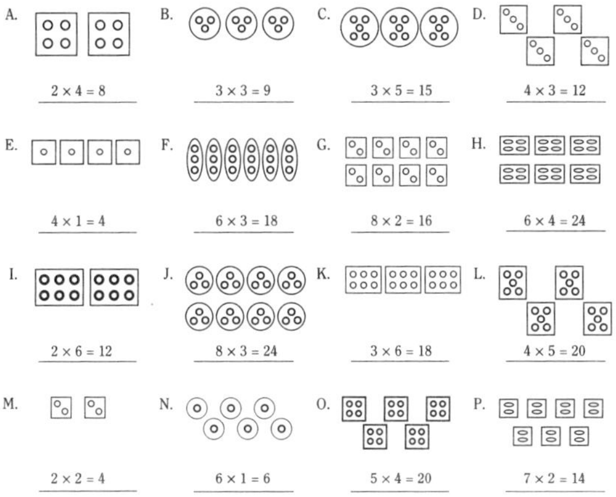

Super challange: Drawings will vary but check to make sure students have show 5 groups of 7 items.

Page 34

Write a multiplication sentence for each addition sentence.

A. **5+5+5=15** — 3 × 5 = 15

B. **6+6+6+6=24** — 4 × 6 = 24

C. **8+8=16** — 2 × 8 = 16

D. **2+2+2+2=8** — 4 × 2 = 8

E. **7+7+7=21** — 3 × 7 = 21

F. **4+4+4+4=16** — 4 × 4 = 16

G. **9+9+9=27** — 3 × 9 = 27

H. **5+5+5+5+5=25** — 5 × 5 = 253

I. **3+3+3+3+3=15** — 5 × 3 = 15

J. **10+10+10+10=40** — 4 × 10 = 40

K. **1+1+1+1+1=5** — 5 × 1 = 5

L. **11+11+11=33** — 3 × 11 = 33

M. **8+8+8+8=32** — 4 × 8 = 32

N. **0+0+0+0=0** — 4 × 0 = 0

O. **12+12+12+12=48** — 4 × 12 = 48

P. **9+9+9+9=36** — 4 × 9 = 36

Super challange: 6 + 6 + 6 + 6 = 4 × 6 = 24

Page 35

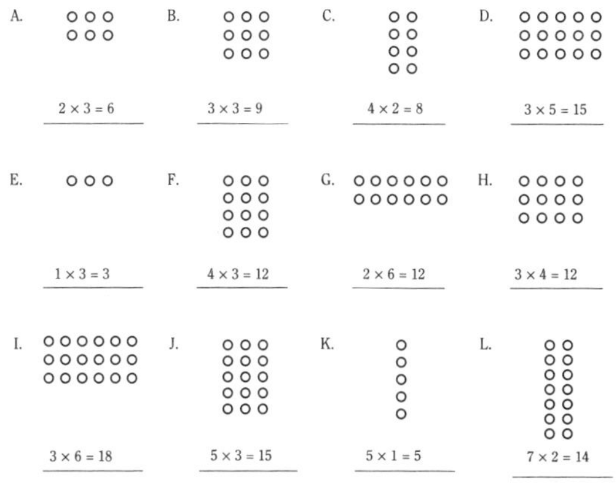

Super challange: There were 4 × 6 = 24 people in the photo

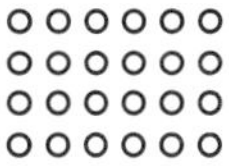

Page 36

66 x 9 = 594; 94 x 8 = 752; 88 x 7 = 616; 91 x 8 = 728; 98 x 8 = 784; 99 x 6 = 594; 68 x 8 = 544; 84 x 9 = 756; 90 x 9 = 810; 89 x 6 = 534; 68 x 7 = 476; 38 x 2 = 76; 95 x 5 = 475; 82 x 3 = 246; 97 x 6 = 582; 88 x 9 = 792; 97 x 9 = 873; 92 x 7 = 644; 56 x 5 = 280; 81 x 4 = 324; 68 x 9 = 612; 90 x 8 = 720; 79 x 4 = 316; 11 x 9 = 99; 87 x 9 = 783; 99 x 9 = 891; 79 x 8 = 632; 74 x 9 = 666; 79 x 9 = 711; 69 x 9 = 621; 82 x 9 = 738; 71 x 8 = 568

Taking It Further: a. 9; **b.** 7; **c.** 6

Page 37

45 x 22 = 990; 89 x 23 = 2047; 75 x 13 = 975; 68 x 26 = 1768
80 x 26 = 2080; 61 x 23 = 1403; 75 x 23 = 1725; 48 x 48 = 2304
96 x 42 = 4032; 77 x 23 = 1771; 49 x 71 = 3479; 24 x 20 = 480
96 x 26 = 2496; 65 x 13 = 845; 45 x 31 = 1395; 54 x 28 = 1512
34 x 28 = 952; 47 x 23 = 1081; 59 x 29 = 1711; 16 x 36 = 576
55 x 52 = 2860; 65 x 21 – 1365; 27 x 57 = 1539; 45 x 22 = 990

Taking It Further: a. 2; b. 1; c. 5

Page 38

1. 20 buttons; **2.** 56 buttons; **3.** 30 mice
4. 126 buttons; **5.** 8 buttons
Super Challenge: 6 teams

Page 39

57 x 73 – 4161; 98 x 34 = 3332; 23 x 13 = 299; 30 x 42 = 1260;
21 x 61 = 1281; 44 x 20 = 880; 87 x 33 = 2871; 79 x 12 = 948; 81 x 14 = 1134; 55 x 13 = 715; 58 x 42 = 2436; 25 x 13 = 325; 60 x 33 = 1980; 61 x 11 = 671; 72 x 32 = 2304; 41 x 23 = 943; 16 x 34 = 544; 53 x 73 = 3869; 27 x 34 = 918; 71 x 17 = 1207; 49 x 52 = 2548; 83 x 17 = 1411; 25 x 46 = 1150; 95 x 36 = 3420; 25 x 17 = 425; 62 x 12 = 744; 23 x 45 = 1035; 26 x 35 = 910; 37 x 11 = 407; 24 x 20 = 480

Page 40
Students should follow these numbers:
13, 7, 3, 9, 19, 23, 11, 5, 17, 67, 33, 25, 27, 35, 39, 37, 23, 57, 47, 43, 21, 15, 39, 29

Page 41
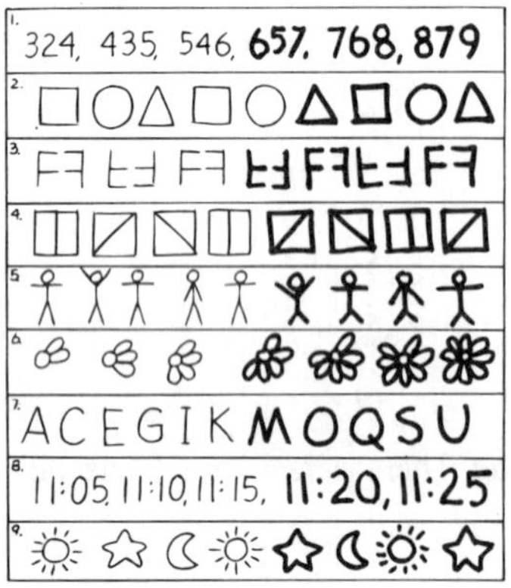

Page 42
1. 23, 26, 29; **2.** 37, 39, 41; **3.** 32, 37, 42;
4. 81, 88, 95; **5.** 59, 70, 81
Super challange: Answers will vary.

Page 43
1. 1; **2.** 4; **3.** 22; **4.** 26; **5.** 34
6. 57; **7.** 115; **8.** 124; **9.** 60; **10.** 215
How can you make the number seven even?
Take away the "s."

Page 44
Drawings will vary, but check to make sure students can visualise and estimate the relative size of the containers.

Page 45
Answers will vary, but check to make sure the lines drawn are approximately correct
A. approx 4 glasses, **B.** approx 3 glasses
C. approx 2 glasses **D.** approx 6 to 8 glasses
Order: D: 1; A: 2; B: 3; C: 2

Page 46
1. 9R1; **2.** 3R3
3. 4R0; **4.** 5R0
5. 2R0; **6.** 6R1
7. 3R0; **8.** 9R2
9. 6R0; **10.** 4R3

Page 47
10, 10, 10 **Extra:** 2

Page 48
14 ÷ 7 = 2; 28 ÷ 7 = 4; 63 ÷ 7 = 9; 49 ÷ 7 = 7
84 ÷ 7 = 12; 70 ÷ 7 = 10; 21 ÷ 7 = 3; 42 ÷ 7 = 6
7 ÷ 7 = 1; 35 ÷ 7 = 5; 77 ÷ 7 = 11; 56 ÷ 7 = 8
70 ÷ 7 = 10; 63 ÷ 7 = 9; 14 ÷ 7 = 2; 28 ÷ 7 = 4
14 ÷ 7 = 2; 7 ÷ 7 = 1; 77 ÷ 7 = 11; 63 ÷ 7 = 9
77 ÷ 7 = 11; 56 ÷ 7 = 8; 7 ÷ 7 = 1; 35 ÷ 7 = 5
Taking It Further: 10 squares

Page 49
4 ÷ 4 = 1; 28 ÷ 4 = 7; 36 ÷ 4 = 9; 16 ÷ 4 = 4
8 ÷ 4 = 2; 32 ÷ 4 = 8; 20 ÷ 4 = 5; 12 ÷ 4 = 3
40 ÷ 5 = 8; 20 ÷ 5 = 4; 5 ÷ 5 = 1; 30 ÷ 5 = 6
15 ÷ 5 = 3; 10 ÷ 5 = 2; 35 ÷ 5 = 7; 45 ÷ 5 = 9

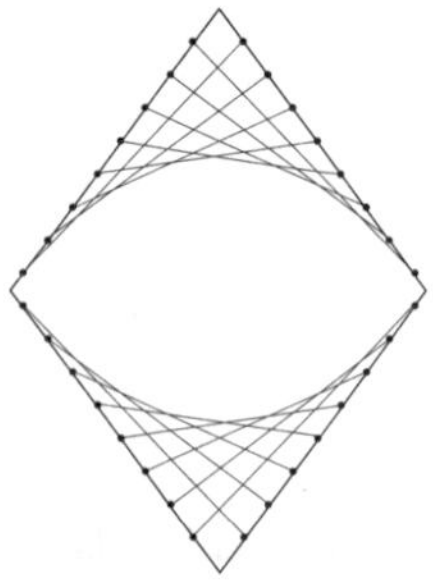

Taking It Further: 10

Page 50
14 ÷ 6 = 2R2; 15 ÷ 9 = 1R6; 86 ÷ 7 = 12R2; 41 ÷ 6 = 6R5
37 ÷ 6 = 6R1; 33 ÷ 9 = 3R6; 15 ÷ 2 = 7R1; 23 ÷ 6 = 3R5
13 ÷ 3 = 4R1; 54 ÷ 7 = 7R5; 45 ÷ 7 = 6R3; 15 ÷ 8 = 1R7
66 ÷ 9 = 7R3; 63 ÷ 8 = 7R7; 28 ÷ 3 = 9R1; 33 ÷ 7 = 5R5
19 ÷ 2 = 9R1; 53 ÷ 6 = 8R5; 27 ÷ 5 = 5R2; 62 ÷ 7 = 8R6
76 ÷ 9 = 8R4; 80 ÷ 9 = 8R8; 17 ÷ 4 = 4R1; 11 ÷ 6 = 1R5

Page 51
	See	Hear	Smell	Touch	Taste
	✓	✓	✓	✓	
	✓				
	✓		✓	✓	✓
	✓		✓		✓
	✓	✓		✓	

Now graph how many senses you used for each object.

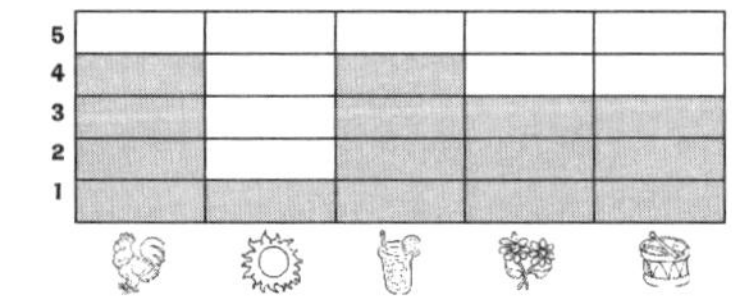

Page 52
A. Sunday; **B.** 89; **C.** Monday; **D.** 24; **E.** 79; **F.** 22
Super challange: Sunday, Tuesday, Saturday.

Page 53
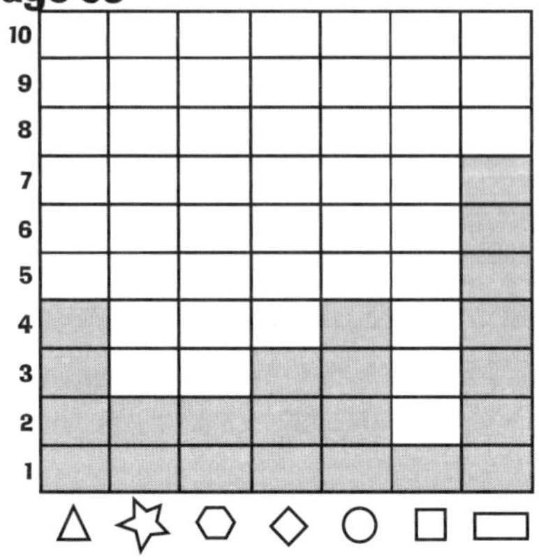

The rectangle